PLAYING DOCTOR

PART TWO: RESIDENCY

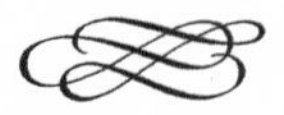

JOHN LAWRENCE

This is a work of non-fiction. All of it happened. These are my recollections, memories, and opinions. Names and places have often been altered. Some events have been compressed. The dialogue in the book is either verbatim or recreated to the best of my recollection. If the words are not exact, then the spirit and meaning of them are represented as accurately as possible. This book is absolutely not intended as a substitute for the advice of a medical professional.

Paperback ISBN: 978-1-7355072-3-1

eBook ISBN: 978-1-7355072-4-8

Edited by Anne Cole Norman

Cover Design by Caroline Johnson

Created with Vellum

CONTENTS

For Chandler, Nico, Mattias & Luca

INTRODUCTION

Since this book chiefly discusses medical training, I'd like to shout out to all the people in healthcare. There is not enough ink in the thousands of pharmaceutical company pens I received from drug reps to write the volumes of heroic stories I witnessed over the years. The world of healthcare is filled with people who personify dedication, compassion and hard work.

I was constantly surrounded by mentors in every aspect of medicine who were, quite simply, amazing. And as much as I might joke in these pages about different medical specialties, I respect them all. I was very fortunate to be taught by wonderful residents, attending physicians and supervisors. Thank you for your teaching and your much needed patience.

While my writing does tend towards the tongue-in-cheek, please know that I have so much gratitude for the teachers, friends, and supporters I have worked with throughout my years in medicine. The medical community is chock full of kindhearted, hard-working, hard-playing, incredible people and we should all be grateful for the work they do—few people will ever know the level of commitment, the time or the caring that those people devote to their patients.

My comments in the book, often glib or flippant, come from my own frustrations at struggling to live up to the high standards set by everyone around me.

PROLOGUE

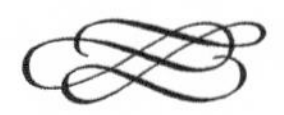

WHERE I CONFIRM I DON'T KNOW ENOUGH TO BE A DOCTOR

When we left off the tales of my nascent medical career in *Playing Doctor, Part One,* I had just graduated medical school and was cycling through Italy with my friend Scott, mostly ignoring his complaints of chest pain. He started grumbling about this tenderness after we spent the night camping in a dirt parking lot. His actual words as he clutched his chest that morning were, "I feel like I'm having a stroke."

First of all, he had never had a stroke, so how would he know what it felt like? Secondly, I was the doctor—and a brand-new doctor at that. So, between the two of us, if anybody would recognize a stroke, *I* would. And I knew that strokes happened in your head, not your chest. So, there was no reason for him to be complaining about having a stroke.

After asking a few medical questions *(Did you hurt yourself making a diving catch for the frisbee last night?),* I dismissed his pain as some tight muscles caused by sleeping on uneven ground. So, despite Scott's carping on about his chest, we kept riding, about a hundred miles a day. And all seemed fine, at least in the world of cycling, because even with his discomfort, Scott continued to be much faster than me.

But there was something wrong with Scott. And I missed it.

Unbeknownst to us, Scott was riding faster than me with only one fully-functioning lung—an embarrassing fact highlighting that I'm not a very strong cyclist. But more relevantly to this book (and perhaps Scott's well-being), my very first medical decision as a doctor, not having Scott evaluated for a collapsed lung, was a potentially fatal blunder. It was a mistake that emphasized just how much I required more medical training (my bike racing career was obviously going nowhere). Fortunately for any future patients (but not Scott), my residency training started a few days later.

To be fair to Scott, he rarely ever complains about pain. He once coached a ski race camp, bouncing across glaciers on skis while carrying heavy backpacks and equipment, mere days after cracking a vertebra in his spine. And I'll do myself some justice to boot: the questions I peppered Scott with when he experienced the initial discomfort were all related to trauma, as I did think to rule out a pneumothorax.

But more on Scott and his spontaneously collapsing lung later.

For those of you who missed my first book in this series, *Playing Doctor, Part One: Medical School,* I'll catch you up: I was a liberal arts-educated student who started medical school right after suffering two bike-induced traumatic head injuries. The first one landed me in the hospital with a minor bleed in my brain. A few weeks later I crashed again. It was the day before medical school started and the accident left me torn and bloodied at the base of a tree with another concussion. The combined head traumas resulted in something known as second impact syndrome.

Second impact syndrome (increased swelling from head trauma before a prior concussion subsides) left me with a lack of short-term memory, an inability to concentrate, severe exhaustion and thunderous headaches. Second impact syndrome can also cause death. So, considering the possible outcomes, my dealing with amnesia, fatigue, and headaches was like winning the lottery.

There were no overt advantages however, to attending medical school with short term memory loss and an inability to stay awake. I barely survived the first semester, achieving the lowest grade in the class on our first anatomy exam. But I made it through two years of book learning with a lot of help from the study notes of my brilliant girl I was dating at the time—she then wisely dumped me and married an orthopedic surgeon.

Despite continually questioning if I was fit to be a doctor (*Can anyone else remember the names of the bones in the body?*), I completed medical school's clinical years, graduated somewhere in the top half of the class, and received a piece of paper stating that I was a doctor.

That was medical school—apart from a few more bike crashes and several injuries I left out of book one, such as a cracked pelvic bone. The important item was that despite my injuries, insecurities and ongoing difficulty memorizing anything without continual review, I managed to graduate and against expectations (my own and others), was on the path to becoming a physician.

Now it was time to start residency—the training you do after medical school, because as illustrated above by my inability to make wise decisions, medical school graduates need more training if they are to properly treat patients.

After much reflection, and admitting I was not serious enough about medicine to pursue a rigorous residency, I applied to Family Practice programs, which only required three additional years of training—surgical or other specialties required five to seven years. I figured I would leave after one year to pursue a career in film while moonlighting in some sort of "doc-in-the-box" urgent care setting. A decision perhaps rivaled in poor planning by my decision to apply to medical school in the first place.

The deeper reason for the Family Practice decision was that during medical school I really enjoyed my elective clinical rotations working in the Telluride Medical Center (Colorado). At the time, the clinic only hired Family Practice doctors. So, I decided I needed the family practice degree to eventually move to Telluride and work in the medical center, along with joining *Médecins sans Frontières (Doctors Without Borders)*, making independent films and producing community theater shows.

I know, all that sounds quite silly to say aloud. If there was a strategic director in my life, he or she needed to be replaced. However, I did go on to work as a doctor for twenty years. I first became the physician and medical director of an urgent care clinic where I practiced traditional western medicine. Years later I opened a functional and regenerative medicine clinic with an exceptional acupuncturist friend, learning a whole new approach to health and wellness that was more aligned with my personal beliefs.

During those same years, and with a *lot* of help from friends, I coordinated and donated medical supplies to a clinic in Tanzania (I had been invited to be the team doctor for my friend, Paralympian Chris Waddell, as he scouted routes to ascend Mt. Kilimanjaro in a hand cycle); produced and directed an independent film (*The Cyclist)* which was accepted to several film festivals; had a small role in a film directed by academy award winning director Danny Boyle (*127 Hours*); produced and acted in sold-out community theater shows; and was fortunate enough to meet and eventually marry an amazing woman with whom I've been blessed to have three wonderful children. Score one for exceeding what you set your mind to.

NOW BACK TO THE WEEKS JUST AFTER MEDICAL SCHOOL. THERE I was, a socially inept, medical doctor making diagnostic gaffes.

Fortunately, I was on the cusp of my Residency training—the years between med school and working as a fully trained doctor. Those are the years which we will explore in these next books, years that are essential to medical training and in my case, years that probably should have been extended.

WHY RESIDENCY?

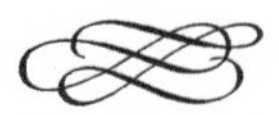

BECAUSE WHAT YOU DON'T KNOW WILL HURT SOMEONE

Fresh out of medical school with my long-awaited M.D. degree, I went on an invigorating cycling trip to Italy with my adventurous friend Scott. The trip concluded with him lying in a hospital bed back in Utah with a chest tube keeping his lung inflated.

It was the night before my intern year started (the first year of Residency), and I sat next to his bed, hunched over my Advanced Cardiac Life Support (ACLS) textbook attempting to memorize the protocols I would be tested on several hours later. The protocols that included identifying and treating a collapsed lung—the very diagnosis I had missed, and the reason Scott was lying in the hospital bed with a tube sticking out of his chest. If missing a major diagnosis exemplified *why* residency training was needed, then I was right where I needed to be.

If anything, it was apropos that my intern year did not start with a good night's sleep, healthy breakfast, or shower, given not much would change during the next years. Instead, I was already in the hospital, dreading having to face Annette (Scott's mother) to explain why Scott's lung was collapsed. I was rightfully nervous because weighing in at around 100 pounds (pure muscle), standing around five feet tall (in heels), and playing at least four sports a day, Annette could easily kick my ass.

Questions would likely arise as to what shenanigans we had created that flattened his lung (answer, none). I could not explain why his lung had deflated, so I looked like an idiot. I was supposed to be a doctor—Scott's family had attended the graduation ceremony that awarded me my M.D.—so how could I not identify something so important as a spontaneously collapsing lung? Well, now I could. My medical education was already flourishing, mere hours from starting residency, which was good, because I needed to outgrow my confused reputation.

To be fair, even real doctors miss pneumothoraces. But let's revisit Scott's case as it highlights why we need to attend residency training (beyond actually learning the specialty that you are going into).

Scott is the same college friend from Book One who had been arrested for disturbing the peace in France and subsequently kicked out of the country; who was later arrested for bungee jumping off the Golden Gate Bridge; and is now a senior partner at a boutique law firm. At the time of the lung collapse, however, we were bicycling together through Italy, ostensibly training for our amateur community races. Scott won races. I specialized in falling off my bike.

One morning Scott said he was having chest pains. I tossed out a few questions (medical questions about his chest, not merely breakfast related queries) and decided that he probably had developed some muscle pain due to our camping out on uneven ground. And we kept riding.

On the flight home, however, Scott's chest pain increased. That was likely because his chest wall was being sucked inward with the pressure changes, potentially causing a fatal tension pneumothorax.

You see, normally the outer, slippery lining of your lung is essentially sealed to your chest wall—like two plates of glass stuck together with water between them. If air gets in between your chest wall and that lining, breaking the seal, your lung can deflate —called a pneumothorax. If the pressure intensifies, as it does when you're flying in an airplane, then the internal pressure potentially sucks your lung into a crinkled little ball, and you cannot breathe—that's what was happening to Scott's lung during the flight home.

The above description is a bit simplified, but what potentially happens as the internal pressure changes pull everything sideways in a person's chest (called a tension pneumothorax) is that you risk complete cardiopulmonary failure, i.e., your heart and lungs cannot function. You die. Fortunately, Scott, who only needed one lung to ride faster than me, was fine, despite being quite sweaty and uncomfortable for the flight.

At home in Utah, Scott's girlfriend Rachel, a far savvier clinician than me, had dragged Scott to the hospital ER because he was having a hard time breathing while they were hiking together. And no, she's not a doctor, just a super intelligent woman who attended business school where apparently, they teach you that people with chest pain who feel short of breath should be evaluated in hospital, not treated to paninis and espresso at roadside Italian cafes.

In the ER, much to everyone's surprise, despite having normal oxygen levels, it turned out Scott had a completely collapsed lung. And I, the newest doctor in town, had missed it.

Now, to be fair, who rides a hundred miles, up and down hills, with a collapsed lung? Nobody, that's who. Except for the cycling-obsessed, pain-in-the-ass friend I happened to be trying to keep up with while both my lungs supposedly functioned.

But thanks to Scott and his overachieving aerobic status, I would never forget this pearl of medical wisdom: *You miss every pneumothorax you don't think of*. Or something like that. You get the idea: you need to remember to think of a pneumothorax in the first place, whenever someone is having trouble breathing, or chest pain.

And I had asked Scott questions related to a pneumothorax because it *had* crossed my mind: *Did you hit the steering wheel of our rented Fiat Punto during an e-brake slide?*

Did you land hard on the sand for an acrobatic Frisbee catch?

Do you feel short of breath?

But he had not experienced any chest trauma that would typically be the cause of a collapsed lung, and instead, only kept saying he felt like it was a stroke. So, I dismissed the lung collapsing idea, thought the stroke descriptor was completely misplaced, and missed the diagnosis altogether.

It turns out, wonder of the human design, your lung can *spontaneously* collapse! Who knew? I did, now, a bit belatedly.

Scott's pulmonary mess proved to me that I suffered from a righteously imposed imposter syndrome—the strong, and now validated belief that I really didn't know what I was doing medically, and therefore had no right to be a doctor. I previously harbored this affliction, as I never really planned on being a doctor and then attended medical school with a liberal arts education. While I had been studying the arts, literature and history, all the pre-med students were busy learning about things like cellular biology, topics with actual relevance to treating the human body. *And* then came the multiple traumatic head injuries that resulted in a lack of decent working memory. My particular set of circumstances always left me feeling that I was behind all the other students and residents who could actually recall what they learned during our medical training.

Then my judgment almost killed Scott—thereby confirming that my feelings of inadequacy were grounded in reality, not merely imposter syndrome. And now I am supposed to take care of patients? Not if they learn about that mixed medical history. There would be a whole lot of, "*Yes, I'd prefer to see that doctor over there, or that one, or—in fact, any of them besides this brain-addled twit who already forgot medical school and almost killed his friend...anyone else in the hospital will do."*

Ironically, I've heard that many successful doctors deal with similar self-doubts. Maybe all residents felt that way. But they sure looked more confident; in fact, they not only looked, sounded, and acted like they knew exactly what they were doing—I'm also pretty certain that the "M.D." on their nametag was in a much larger and bolder font than mine.

In any case, while it did heighten my sense of being a poser in a white coat, missing Scott's pneumothorax did result in me never overlooking one again. Future patients of mine could thank Scott and his spontaneously collapsing chest for helping make me that little bit more vigilant regarding pneumothoraces.

Many years later, in fact, my father-in-law would call to see if I could examine his ribs. He had slipped walking on black ice the day before and slammed down onto the pavement. Being a hard-headed Swede of Viking stock, and never one to complain, he had very reluctantly gone into an urgent care clinic for evaluation. The doctor took some X-rays, told him that his ribs were bruised, and reassured him that despite not being able to breathe well, he and his ribs were otherwise fine. He informed the doctor that he was due to travel, wanting to be sure it was safe to fly and that his ribs were not broken. Once again, they assured him he was fine.

So when he took time to visit me in my clinic the following day, wanting a second opinion on his ribs, I knew he must be hurting. Another medical pearl to remember when a patient (or parent of a patient) tells you they feel the previous doctor missed something, it's a red flag. People know their health and bodies (or their kid's health) better than you ever will. Your ears should therefore prick up reflexively when they hear something like, "I think the other doctor missed something."

I could tell something was not right just by looking at my

father-in-law; bruised ribs hurt tremendously—but something felt, or looked, awry.

I checked his blood oxygen saturation level—which was normal. And maybe somewhere, deep in the recesses of my dim brain, something reminded me of Scott being slightly short of breath all those years ago, also with a normal heart rate and oxygen level—and my father-in-law is also a cyclist, which changes the paradigm as cyclists have very healthy aerobic systems, meaning their vital signs might be normal, despite being somewhat compromised.

I dug out a stethoscope and listened to his chest. The left side sounded fine with normal breath sounds. But the air movement sounded ever so slightly diminished on the right side.

I sent him to the hospital diagnosed with a pneumothorax. A few hours later a scan confirmed the pneumothorax and broken ribs, and a chest tube was inserted to re-inflate his lung. To be fair, cracked ribs can be hard to pick up on X-ray, and the lung might have deflated more for me to pick it up. But just maybe, I was more suspicious to begin with after having missed Scott's diagnosis years prior.

And that type of experiential learning is exactly why we have residency: to learn how to think and act as a doctor by repeatedly seeing—and caring for—many medical cases; not merely providing hospitals with cheap labor sources, which is originally why I thought we were there.

So, residency training would provide all sorts of learning opportunities where you made mistakes and almost killed patients so that later, when you're practicing on your own, you would have learned from practical experiences. That's not exactly how it works, but I will admit, residency training, despite the hours and stress, is good for all parties involved.

EVERY JULY, THE MOST RECENT MEDICAL SCHOOL GRADUATES ARRIVE at teaching hospitals to start their residency training. All of the most skilled and proficient residents have just left to work as real doctors, and the hospital is now filled with inexperienced interns. So, if you're looking ahead to book a hospital stay, July is not the best time to be admitted to a teaching hospital.

In the United States, the first year of residency is called the intern year. Why? Because you don't deserve to be called a resident yet. That is actually what I thought until, well, about ten minutes ago when I decided to look up the history of interns and residents.

I really did think interns were just differentiated from being called residents because we had not earned that right yet. The medical world thrives on hierarchy; to the point that some medical programs determine the length of your medical white coat based on your years of training. Everyone immediately has a visual cue to identify your social status: medical students wear very short and shabby brown or baby-blue blazers in order to visibly stick out as peons; whereas Medical Doctors have earned the right to wear a white gown (sounds like a prom), whose length increases with years of training until, as an attending physician, you traipse through the hospital with your gown trailing three meters behind, carried by pre-med students, and wearing a tiara. Ok, the last part isn't really true. And the University of Utah, friendly program that it is, outfits all medical students, residents, and attending physicians in matching length white coats regardless of your status. But first-year residents are still called interns.

Turns out that first-year residents are nicknamed "interns" because you are entering what was called your internship (apparently nobody could afford creative copywriters). Back at the turn of the century (20th century, that is) someone decided that it made sense for graduates of medical school to receive a bit more training before being let loose with their own practice. Evidently, this foresight came about with me in mind.

Terms like Resident, Intern, or House Officer had very literal meanings dating back to the late 1800s.

Young physicians were actually required to live at the hospital, i.e. take up "residence" in or near the building where they practiced. And at the University of Michigan, where their first hospital was inside a converted house, the very first resident physicians were truly "house" officers.

The first young physicians to be called "interns" were hired in 1899, and were paid $125 a year, and salaries have not increased very much since.

Those interns also received room and board in the hospital or nearby houses—we did not.

And some things don't change. Those first interns were the top students in each graduating medical class, competing fiercely to be chosen to stay on for additional training at the hospital. Competitive fierceness remains alive and well in the medical training world.

If we thought getting into medical school was competitive, well, residency was even more so. The same people who had successfully overcome the odds to get into medical school now competed for acceptance into the most competitive and prestigious residency programs, such as dermatology, radiology, orthopedics, or ophthalmology.

I had been a novelty case, accepted as a liberal arts student to see if I would make it through medical school, and apparently there were residency programs willing to play along to see how far I could survive.

What do you actually do as a medical resident? You write a lot of notes: patient admit notes, daily progress notes, discharge notes, notes to your mom that you will not be visiting for holidays. You continued to rotate through different clinical services, just like medical students, evaluating and treating patients, but now with added responsibilities and increased workloads. On top of anticipating those increased pressures, I still felt I had missed some significant learning in medical school due to my irksome, bike-crash induced, amnesia. So I was feeling pretty nervous approaching my first day working as a resident.

And for those of you more concerned about Scott still lying about in a hospital bed, he healed just fine and was on his bike in no time, winning races and putting my fully functioning lungs to shame.

INTERN YEAR

YOU'RE FINALLY A DOCTOR. NOW WHAT?

In medical school, my personal history (i.e., being the liberal arts-educated student lacking short-term memory from head trauma, who admitted to not being sure about his career choice) granted me a somewhat legitimate excuse for being confused. And being confused as a medical student was mildly tolerated as we were essentially visitors on the clinical wards. Nobody expected us to jump in and start working as doctors—although many impressive med students did just that. But now, mere days after exhausting your visitor's status, it was your real-life job, i.e., you weren't visiting for the experience, you were expected to start working as a trained doctor with real accountability.

The intern year had rightfully earned the reputation as the most grueling year of medical training. The quantity of gruel varied with what type of residency you were doing and where. For example, surgical interns anywhere lived a life no sane person wants to endure. I am still traumatized just thinking of my surgical friends describing their horrific intern year, mostly battling to stay awake during surgeries, and barely able to physically function *if* they made it home late at night—as in, not able to make themselves a snack, just collapsing inside the front door of their apartment, sleeping for a couple of hours on the floor or couch, before returning to the hospital.

A family practice intern, however, in, say, Reno, had time to ski several days a week. But, that's Reno, and that was why I did not even place their program on my residency match list. I was staying in Salt Lake City at the University of Utah Family Practice program which, for family practice programs, was a bit more rigorous and stricter with their requirements and average call structure; in terms of hours worked, we were on par with all the internal medicine programs being on call every three to four nights.

What was so crazy about intern year? Mostly long hours without a break. You were responsible for all the hospital grunt work, so there was never time to complete your responsibilities, and with a schedule that required you be in the hospital for call nights, you spend almost one-third of your nights, and all but one weekend a month, in the hospital. It adds up, and you feel beaten down.

Truthfully, most people work hard: restaurant employees, laborers, first-year corporate lawyers and bankers, anyone at a tech start-up, television writing staff—all of them endure long work weeks. And let's not even start with parenting, now there's a great job: no time off, zero pay and ungrateful little whelps yelling at you. And let's not even start with parenting, now there's a great job: no time off, zero pay and ungrateful little whelps yelling at you. I suffered PTSD after our first child's sleepless first year in the world—and I was not putting in close to the hours that my wife was during those long months. But I'm here to bitch about being an intern, not whine about parenting hours—you can read parenting blogs for that experience while we carry on with exploring medical training.

This seems like a decent segue into discussing the resident call situation. Being "on-call" refers to being the doctor, or team, that is called when there is a patient to admit to the hospital, or a patient in the hospital that needs to be evaluated, or a phone call taken from nurses or the ER. On-call, or a call night, typically meant it was your turn to spend the night in hospital overseeing current patients and admitting new ones that showed up needing care. Occasionally, certain rotations allowed "home call," which meant you went home, but were called back in to admit patients, or for emergencies.

There have been newspaper articles written, and changes attempted, regarding how many hours medical residents are allowed to work in the hospital—awake or otherwise. There's awareness of the long hours worked, as well as documented mistakes that might have been the result of those excessive hours causing fatigue. As mentioned, many people work long hours—nobody ever said it was healthy, but what is ideal and what is required do not always align. And like everyone with demanding jobs, families, and lives, residents just do their work.

But then one night in 1984, Libby Zion was admitted to a hospital. She was eighteen years old, shaking, and feverish. She was treated by junior residents who had been working long hours. Libby's case was complicated. There was uncertainty as to what was causing her symptoms. And the hospital team was unaware of the combination of prescribed and recreational medicines and drugs she had taken. She was treated with medicines to calm her shaking, but her condition worsened. Her fever rose to 107 degrees. Libby went into cardiac arrest and the medical team was unable to resuscitate her. It was a terrible and sad case.

Libby's father, a *New York Times* legal reporter, was outraged. His daughter had been treated by an intern and junior residents working long hours, and with minimal involvement from the attending physician who should have overseen her care. He channeled his fury into a legal battle regarding his daughter's death, and into what became a decades long battle to reform the hours medical residents were allowed to work.

The case of Libby Zion is documented, complicated and has been extensively debated. She died due to what is now believed to be serotonin-syndrome, which occurs when your body has too much serotonin, a neurotransmitter that, in simple terms, sends messages between cells. Serotonin affects your whole body and your mood. Many anti-depressants and recreational drugs work by increasing the amount of serotonin in the brain. Too much serotonin however causes too much cell stimulation, which can cause fevers, shaking, seizures and in extreme cases, lead to death. Serotonin-syndrome is something we were trained to watch for due to it being potentially fatal if not treated quickly.

It is however easy to say what should have been done retrospectively. It's difficult however to put yourself in the place of the doctors working that night. I believe medical residents, with knowledge of the case, can scour their brains for how they might have acted differently and wonder if they might have, in good faith, made the same decisions on a busy night with multiple patients to evaluate and treat.

I have two comments on the general subject. First, mistakes happen. I don't care how rested, or how exhausted someone is; people make mistakes. I have known nurses, fresh on their shift with abundant sleep, to mistakenly inject an overdose of medicine into a patient's I.V. line. Likewise, I have repeatedly witnessed residents perform surgeries perfectly when they have not had more than three hours of combined sleep, per night, for weeks on end. I'm not saying it's healthy or wise, but that was the reality of the medical system.

Mistakes happen, but the medical community was justly expected to be perfect—which still does not guarantee perfect outcomes. It is an unfair standard for any group of people—but when you're the one person out of 10,000 that received the wrong dose of medicine...well, at that point, 99.9999 percent perfect doesn't provide solace to anyone--even less so when it's your child, or your pregnant wife, who suffers because of an error. It's horrible. It's absolutely horrible, and devastating, for everyone involved, none more than the patient and family.

Medical residents, students, and doctors must live with the fearful idea that almost certainly you will one day, unwittingly, make a mistake that negatively affects another person. Even years later, without sleep deprivation as an excuse, I was haunted by the idea that I was making medical decisions to the best of my ability, but perhaps inadvertently committing some mistake, missing a diagnosis, missing a lab value, missing something that would, however innocently, in my best effort to provide safe and beneficial care, hurt someone.

It was, and is, a nauseating thought that anything you did in your job, which aims to help people, caused pain, suffering, damage, or worse. I, and most doctors I know, wrestle emotionally with the fact that a treatment might not have worked well, let alone considering it resulted in a bad outcome. And that is another frustrating reality, sometimes the correct treatment just does not work.

Second point: While there was an imposed limit (supposedly) on the number of hours residents were permitted to work in the hospital, it was not reasonable, feasible, acceptable, or even possible as a medical resident, to announce to your team that you had completed your allowable hours for the week, and were now going to go home, drink a beer, and take a nap. It would be completely outside the realm of reality for a resident to walk out of the hospital after their 80th work hour for the week (the maximum hours a resident was supposedly allowed to work in the hospital). You would receive a better reaction if you explained that you were actually the Easter Bunny, and were now going home to paint eggs for the night.

Residency was not a union. Residents were cheap labor, and needed to work in order to learn, to fund the hospitals, and to do the necessary chores—too bad for you if the hours violated child labor laws after you knowingly signed up for this nonsense.

And the long hours, it was argued, did serve a purpose: medical residents have a massive amount to learn in a relatively short amount of time. And while book learning continued, the experience of thinking and acting like a physician required repetition; and you only got the experience of live repetition on a volume and variety of medical patients and problems by being in the hospital and clinics for long periods of time.

Think about how many times a professional tennis player practices hitting a forehand during training—way more than resident doctors practice treating a hypoxic child during all their years of learning. I'm not sure that analogy makes sense, but you get the idea, we needed to practice by seeing the real thing repeatedly in training, to handle it properly once graduated.

To be fair, while 120-hour workweeks happened, they were rare. Even the 80-hour workweek was not a regular occurrence for family practice residents. It was, however, typical for surgical residents. The residency programs justified the excess work hours through accounting magic. Hollywood studio accountants shake their abacus and *voilà*, the most successful films in box office history never made a profit and therefore had none to share. The administration calculating resident hospital hours, having attended the same accounting school as their Hollywood counterparts, crunched numbers and informed us that on average we were barely in the hospital and probably shouldn't even be paid.

We weren't expecting profits, but the same sort of manipulative arguments, some mumbo jumbo about working seven days a week, and averaging the hours worked, including a weekend off last month and a vacation, somehow meant you were taking way too much time off and actually needed to spend more time in the hospital to come close to the allowable 80-hours—and your clinic hours didn't count against hospital hours—and remember when you walked from your car to the clinic? You had a break right there, so stop complaining.

The truth as I saw it, was that mistakes in hospitals were not usually due to residents screwing up because they were tired. There is a large checks and balance system in place to prevent fatigue or ignorance from taking charge—two prized intern characteristics. Fortunately, there were numerous people to oversee an intern's actions: nurses, pharmacists, attending physicians, your senior resident, all of whom should technically oversee something like a written order for a medicine or treatment before it was administered. But occasionally mistakes were made. And mistakes made by medical residents were sometimes due to hubris, not fatigue.

That's right, not only was medical training largely based on the Socratic teaching method, the screw-ups and blunders also occurred within a Greek tragedy framework—pride before a fall. Residents with too much pride to ask for help, or residents who were too much of a cowboy (i.e., reckless), were eventually humbled by peers, or made a mistake that truly mortified them.

Mistakes occurred at many different levels—nurses not understanding doctor's orders, miscalculating medicines, etc. And I am not saying it was just nurses, they too work a demanding job. My point is that it was not only the residents making mistakes—but they were a worthy scapegoat due to the long hours worked.

The truly embarrassing mishaps took place on a more personal level for the residents, like falling asleep in all sorts of random, inconvenient locations or odd times.

Falling asleep at stop signs and traffic lights while driving home from call nights was so common that the public should be wary driving anywhere near a teaching hospital when the on-call residents are released. Post-call residents should be required to place colorful weather balloons on their cars warning other drivers to steer clear. That is a real lawsuit waiting to happen—a resident dying after falling asleep at the wheel on the way home from being awake for thirty-six hours or crashing into someone else.

And it was not much safer when you arrived home.

I repeatedly put the cordless phone away in the microwave, put shaving cream on my toothbrush, looked in the refrigerator when the phone rang, put the phone back in the refrigerator (perhaps resulting in the previous problem?), and encountered ridiculous cooking problems.

I once threw Swiss cheese onto some bread, added sliced tomatoes in between, and made a peanut butter and jelly sandwich for the next day's lunch while the grilled cheese supposedly cooked. But the damned thing did not turn into grilled cheese. The cheese, apparently some sort of thermodynamically stable substance, simply would not melt. I touched the stove's surface to make sure it was on...and felt heat emanating. It burnt my hand (I really dislike electric range tops).

In my tired state of disbelief, mixed with exhausted, frustrated rage at the cheese's inability to melt, and the pain in my hand, it took me another ten minutes to realize that I had confused the front and back burner dials, front being where the pan was, and not which switch I had turned; the heat radiating from the rear fooled me into believing that the stove was working just fine, but confused why my sandwich failed to cook.

Once the light bulb clicked in that dark space between my ears, the rest fell into place rather nicely: I promptly proceeded to burn both sides of the bread and went to bed hungry with a scorched hand.

I have confirmed that such homestead nonsense was in no way limited to myself; it ran rampant in every resident's life. And to think, those insightful and fatigued abilities of deduction were regularly being called on to evaluate sick and dying patients at four in the morning.

One final note, Libby Zion's death and her father's subsequent battles were not in vain. In 2003, one year after I completed my residency training, a national mandate was issued limiting medical residents to roughly 80-hour work weeks. It's called the Libby Zion Law.

ORIENTATION & THE ART OF MEDICINE

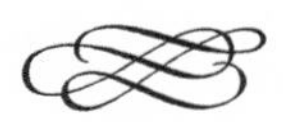

WHERE WE LEARN HOW TO ACT LIKE A DOCTOR. (SUPPOSEDLY)

Fortunately, the week prior to starting on the clinical wards included several days of orientation for the newly arrived interns to receive some instruction before being let loose to scamper through the hospital hallways. First up, the entire intern class from every residency program in the hospital was required to pass an ACLS course (the stuff you do when somebody decides to stop breathing, or their heart stops beating). The hospital realized it would be inappropriate if a patient collapsed inside a building structured around healthcare, and the first person at the scene, a resident doctor, did not know what to do. So, we all took the ACLS course taught by the anesthesiology department.

It was here, in ACLS training, that we rehearsed what to do in "Code" situations, such as using the proper tone when shouting, "Epi! Stat!" You really wanted to nail the calm yet authoritative voice, as we imagined we would soon be commanding life-saving code situations (much more on codes later, some heroic, most not). Regardless of this training, your authoritatively trained voice typically went on holiday during a real code situation.

ACLS training also happened to be where I would relearn to assess and treat a person with a collapsed lung; aka a pneumothorax; aka the pesky, potentially fatal condition I had missed in my friend Scott, who was currently recovering in the hospital with a tube sticking out of his chest.

Good news, with a lot of coaching from our anesthesiology instructors we all passed our ACLS training. What else did we learn in orientation?

We were repeatedly told to respect the hospital nurses because they could save your ass. Quite true. Or make your life miserable. Also true. You would think, however, that acting respectfully should be normal human behavior.

Apparently not.

Every year, some new intern strutted into the hospital, pointed at the M.D. on their nametag and announced, "Me Doctor," then acted as though it was a shiny ticket to boss people around. These attitudes didn't last long. Interns were eventually physically exhausted to the point that there was no energy left to act conceitedly; or they were put in their place by senior residents. No room for self-importance or arrogance—and these personality types were rare anyway. Everyone worked hard.

They also tried teaching us some financial planning during orientation, as we were now to have a modicum of income for our work—not very much—so I didn't listen too closely.

Big mistake.

I'm pretty sure the advice was to max out your 401K and pay off your student loans as quickly as possible. I never started a 401K until many years after graduation. I then cashed it out early, along with maxing out four credit cards, to produce an independent film. Pretty sure that wasn't part of the advice they gave out either—but you can check the film out on Amazon, *The Cyclist*.

There was also some talk addressing how best to pay off your medical school debt—didn't really pay attention to that part of the lecture either. And unsurprisingly, to this day, now twenty-two years later, I'm still paying off those pesky loans.

And then, after receiving our soon-to-be bane of existence, our very own hospital pager (ancient electronic devices that beeped or vibrated with a text message of where to go in the hospital, or a number to call), and signing forms that said we might be paid and fed over the next years, we were cut loose to our respective residency programs.

The next day, every other intern started into their clinical rotations, working as doctors. We family practice residents, however, were special.

The following morning our fellow interns strode through the hospital doors and immediately started performing surgeries, delivering babies, evaluating heart rhythms, sewing up lacerations, diving into their new identity with authority and flair, and staying up on call—but we few, we special few, enjoyed several more days of orientation that included picnics, lectures, drawing colorful stories of our lives, running around outside playing trust games, and sleeping in.

The desired effect was to teach us all the importance of teamwork and to lecture us about the *Art of Medicine*: what it takes to become a *truly* remarkable doctor. As far as I was concerned, it meant more days to play, sleep, and see the sun shining. Did it make us better doctors? I don't think so. But it was fun.

The *Art of Medicine* instructed us to never say something like, "You should check out the rampant case of pancreatitis in room 442." But rather, "Mrs. Smith is a lovely 64-year-old woman with an angry pancreas. You should ask to examine her abdomen. She's in room 442." Referring to patients by their name, not their condition, is an artistic skill taught to primary care physicians.

Specialists were too busy performing medicine to be worried about the arts.

Primary care physicians write pages of chart notes, covering every aspect of the patient's health and wellbeing. They want to document their patient's history of illnesses, diet, psychosocial health, developmental milestones, sexual preferences, special interests, and hobbies.

"Hobbies?" you ask.

Absolutely. First, it allows the billing team to charge a more expensive billing code.

Wait, what? How does that work?

All your doctor visits have billing codes associated with measurements of your time together, the complexities of the problems discussed, and any procedures performed. A very low-level code for a simple problem will pay less than a complex visit. You can also increase billing code levels if you covered several issues in their psychosocial history (like hobbies), and basic physical exam information, like measuring your weight and blood pressure. That's why you get weighed every time you visit the doctor, so they can bill a higher code and get paid more.

Secondly, interviewing patients about their hobbies might provide diagnostic clues. Perhaps, while all the specialists were busy fixing medical issues and likely overlooking the patient's passion for woodworking—the curious primary care doc might clue into that hobby being the source of varnish and paint exposure which caused the patient's lung cancer.

But nobody cared, because by the time the patient had lung cancer, they went right to the specialist anyway. Specialists lacked time for such verbosity, not to mention the patient's woodworking proficiency did not enter their overworked brains as they worked to eliminate the illness.

To be fair, the goal was to teach primary care physicians to warn their patients about potential sources of harm or illness *before* it was an issue, i.e. preventative care—keeping you healthy so you never needed to be treated for lung cancer. As an acupuncturist friend explained to me years later, in traditional Chinese medicine, if a patient becomes ill, then the medical practitioner had failed at their job twenty years earlier.

Meanwhile, the specialist physicians ruthlessly interrogated their interns and medical students with questions such as, "What type of lung cancer would potentially be associated with paint and varnish exposure?" Answer: small cell carcinoma.

At the exact same time, I would be spending seventeen crucial minutes listening to Mr. Peterson tell me about his woodworking tools and lathe collection—minutes that other patients spent waiting for me, minutes I could have used to finally eat lunch.

This was all part of the art of medicine. Primary care physicians were instructed to first applaud the patient for having a hobby (as such activities are good for mental health), and then tell them to avoid too much exposure, so as not to get lung cancer in the first place (preventative medicine at its finest!). And then you ask more questions so you could write more notes and bill higher codes.

We wrote long, long, looooong, notes.

The specialists treated patients; their notes were succinct.

My single favorite note in a medical chart was, *"Pulses present,"* a note written by a surgical resident. He felt no need to elaborate beyond noting, in essence, *the patient is still alive*. Just brilliantly concise.

Not to be outdone, the attending surgeon had signed off on the resident's note by scribbling, *"Agree."* Brevity being the soul of wit, lingerie, and medical efficiency.

And the truly important question: what, pray tell, in the Hippocratic world had befallen me? *I had a favorite medical note?* I was obviously losing my mind.

And I'm being a bit flippant with the specialist vs. primary care bit; specialists do require very precise notes to document their thinking and planning; notes that need to be easily comprehended by anyone new involved in that patient's care—and to cover their ass lest anything go wrong. Meanwhile, I started to feel that a lot of primary care could be done by well-trained mid-level caregivers, like Nurse Practitioners and Physician Assistants. The doctors therefore wanted us to write really long notes to justify our existence. And, yes, admittedly, by writing thousands of those long, painful, notes, it forced you to organize your thinking about patients, and in return to become a better doctor.

But the art of medicine had more to do with handling patients than writing beautiful notes. "Primary care" doctors, so we were told, had to be *really* good in order to care for a wide variety of issues in a compact timeframe. And the way to do this was to listen to your patients—something the art of medicine properly instructed us to do. In fact, we were taught that ninety percent of diagnoses could be made from the history part of the exam, despite that fact that we all wanted to jump to the physical part of examining the patient.

In medical school and residency, we were taught to be efficient with our patient visits, using keen interviewing and effective time management skills. You had mere minutes to figure out why a patient was blessing you with their complaints, so that you could perform a quick, and paradoxically thorough (while often gratuitous) physical exam, so that your office could be paid, and you would not be fired. That is the real art of medicine and the reality of the medical field: see lots of patients in an efficient manner (i.e. several minutes), check enough boxes to be paid, and not miss anything that could lead to a lawsuit.

DURING ORIENTATION WE ALSO VISITED WHAT WOULD BE OUR "clinic" for the next three years. This visit entailed another drug company-sponsored lunch with free pens—something to look forward to for three more years. I almost needed to buy a new chest of drawers just to keep all the free pens I was given that first year.

The clinic was where patients went for regular doctor visits. For family practice doctors, the clinic appointments represented the traditional time to get to know the patient and their family. We were taught that comprehending a patient's family was crucial to understanding the patient.

For instance, where would you start with a woman complaining of fatigue for unknown reasons? Ah, when you used your art of medicine sleuth listening skills and tricked her into admitting she had delivered triplets eleven weeks ago, you gained insight into one possible source of her fatigue.

For the record, that patient dismissed my suggestion that her caring for the three-month-old triplets might be the source of her fatigue as utter nonsense because, as she explained, she already had two other small children, and had never been this tired taking care of either one of them.

Faultless logic.

She never came to see me again.

It was in this clinic environment that we would see a wide variety of patients with whom to hone our skills: sick little kids, geriatric patients, pregnant women, drug seekers, people actually in pain, personality disorders, you name it. We would have time to get to know each patient, and their variety of social issues, so we could completely manage their health care.

At the same time, we would have an attending physician present in the clinic with whom to discuss and learn more about how to best care for each patient.

That was the ivory tower model anyway.

Reality was based upon the clinic making money (i.e. seeing as many patients as possible), and attending physicians having multiple tasks to accomplish, including seeing their own patients, finishing their own charts, and frequently making airline reservations to escape the clinic and its interns' continually asking questions. Practice and theory—the two met less frequently than resident and attending, which was never enough.

Enough orientation—let's start working as a doctor already!

FAMILY PRACTICE SERVICE

WHAT THE F*&# DID I SIGN UP FOR?

The smell. That's what you never forget. Illness, bedpans, urine, blood, vomit, alcohol pads, and industrial disinfectants concoct a witch's brew, *L'Eau-de-Inpatient-Medicine,* which wafts through and infects hospital rooms and hallways.

I'm confident that blindfolded medical residents could identify where they were in a hospital by the scent alone—dead giveaway if you add the sounds. Each floor has its own unique odor, some merely reeking of sterility; but the alcohol pad/bed pan fragrance of a medicine floor haunts me to this day. I can't walk a hospital's medicine floor without a visceral nauseating response.

I should quickly clear up some doctor jargon regarding the term "medicine." In hospitals the words medicine and surgery are specific. There is a divide between residents: surgical versus medical. When medical students first consider applying for residency, the first question asked is, "Are you thinking medicine or surgery?" Meaning, are you going to operate on patients or not? The answer defines both your social status and friends for the next decade. Typically, "medicine" refers to all things non-surgical for adult patients. So, when I say "medicine floor" or "inpatient medicine" it refers to the hospital wards where adult patients are cared for by medicine teams. Surgery, OB, and ICU patients normally have their own designated area in the hospital.

As medical students, we had essentially been guests on each assigned hospital rotation. You observed, you learned, you offered to pick up coffee, you were given responsibilities that felt important—and medical students do a lot of valuable work to help their respective teams.

But now, as medical residents the hospitals were your home for years ahead. You were not visiting; you were not leaving anytime soon; you were responsible for patient care; you were responsible for several thousand pages of paperwork (unless you're from Wyoming, but more about those duty-shirking, lazy, cow-wranglers later); and nobody brought you coffee.

It was time to start work as an intern, a junior doctor, the lowest level doctor, there to do grunt work. Yes, you were low in the pecking order, but you *were* a doctor, nonetheless, embarking on this new adventure with confidence and commanding respect throughout the hospital.

Reality?

Confidence in my medical training was on vacation or likely never existed. Due to my history of head trauma and resulting imposter syndrome, I needed to study and re-study, multiple times, information everyone else seemed to have grasped during medical school. I couldn't pull out details the way other residents seemed able to do. Maybe I had always lacked that skill? Maybe they studied harder than me in their spare hours?

And I certainly didn't hear of anyone else starting his or her medical career with such a magnificent howler as missing their friend's pneumothorax. I was obviously not ready to be a doctor.

But the hospital paging system didn't know any better. On my first day it called out for everyone to hear, *"Dr. Lawrence, room 407, Dr. Lawrence to room 407."*

The first time sounded kind of cool.

"Excuse me," I told a nurse standing nearby, "That page was for me. I'm Dr. Lawrence." Which obviously impressed her as I was likely being summoned to save a life.

She was not impressed. The page was for me to digitally dis-impact stool from a patient's rectum (yup, use my fingers to dig shit out of a patient because it was too packed in to move by itself). So much for the idea of commanding respect. Rectal exams are a good reality check for any ego-driven young physician—which by the way I was not, but it still didn't excuse me from the dis-impaction assignment.

My pager buzzing the first time was similarly exciting—I was being recognized as a doctor. After it went off for the eighteenth time during my first two hours as an intern, I wanted to smash the horrid little apparatus. Our lives were to be plagued by pagers, call nights, and hospital food.

Welcome to the life of a medical intern.

Medical residents' clinical rotations typically matched up with their specialty: Surgeons focused on surgical rotations (general surgery, orthopedics, urology, ENT, Surgical ICU); Internal Medicine interns rotated through adult medicine services like cardiology, nephrology (kidney service), pulmonology (lungs), etc. Pediatric interns focused on pediatric rotations in and out of the hospital, including the ER, and the Pediatric ICU.

Family Practice residents rotated through medical, surgical, pediatric, and obstetric rotations and saw their own clinic patients.

Some Family Practice doctors might eventually work in truly rural locations and be responsible for delivering babies, treating coughs, and performing minor surgeries. They did therefore require a vast sort of experience and would later perfect their skills on the job. Maybe that's why those Wyoming residents always scurried home post-haste without finishing their work. They had to go practice their doctor skills. Aren't you curious why I'm holding a grudge against the Wyoming residents? Soon enough.

My first rotation was called Family Practice Service (FPS), which was just a rebranded month of in-patient medicine, i.e., taking care of adult patients admitted to the hospital. Why did they feel a need to rename the service? In order to differentiate us from the Internal Medicine resident teams because, as I will keep mentioning, we family practice residents were special.

How special? On this, my very first rotation as a real doctor, our entire team was so slow seeing patients admitted to the hospital and writing our notes that the Chief Resident, risking mutiny, took away all our days off. Usually everyone enjoyed one free weekend during the rotation while the other residents cross-covered for you, i.e. took care of your patients. But apparently, we were too slow seeing our own patients, let alone managing to cross-cover, so we all had to come in every day during that first rotation.

I spent the first month of my intern year without a day off, which was obviously quite traumatizing because I'm still grumbling about it all these years later. Surgery residents, meanwhile, scoff at such a paltry number of days worked in a row; they wish they could work more days than the week entailed. I was a wimp, however, and had not applied to be a surgeon for many reasons, some of them reasonable, like working semi-sane hours.

A lack of days off that first month wasn't my only complaint; I quickly learned to *despise* the PA system and my pager, as they all seemed to take personal pleasure in having me run in circles. Although I should more accurately blame the nurses who thought it funny to dial intern's pagers all night long with simple questions, just to break in the new doctors.

I vividly recall sitting down at 3 a.m. in the residents' lounge (lounge is a generous term, we had a couch, bathroom, and single beds in case we had a few minutes to lie down) and taking my shoes off to rest my feet my first weekend on call. Then my pager rang. I called the fourth-floor nursing station, the same one I had just left five minutes ago:

"Hello, this is Dr. Lawrence, I was paged."

"I have an order to give Mrs. Smith in room 413 some Tylenol if she has a headache...."

"Ok."

"She has a headache."

"Uh-huh"

"Can I give her some Tylenol?"

"Well...uh," I tried to think through the catch I might be missing, "That's what the order says, right?"

"Yes."

"So, you're calling to see if you can give her the Tylenol?"

"Yes."

"And the written order is to give her Tylenol if she requests it for a headache?"

"Yes."

"Ok. She has a headache, so, I guess it's ok to let her have the Tylenol."

"Ok. *You're the doctor, if you think it's alright...*" she said, in a tone suggesting I was missing something crucial...maybe the patient had a ruptured brain aneurysm, and I was casually ordering Tylenol without evaluating her? Or...wait...*maybe she's* --

"Is she allergic to Tylenol?"

"No."

I put my shoes back on, walked down the hall and climbed several flights back upstairs, to go see Mrs. Smith in room 413.

"Hi, Mrs. Smith?"

"Are you the Nurse? Can I have my Tylenol already? Why's it taking you so long?"

She had a headache and just wanted her Tylenol.

The nurse could have followed the written orders without my verbal confirmation.

I could have told her to do so over the phone, except I was too nervous as a new intern to miss something crucial that might hurt a patient.

The nurse smiled as I gave the ok for her to follow the simple written order that was designed to save me from visiting every patient in the hospital with a headache who needed some Tylenol. As I walked away after wasting ten precious minutes dealing with that simple Tylenol order that the nurse could have easily handled without paging me, I imagined her giggling with the other nurses, plotting fun ways to torture all the fresh and tense interns.

And somewhere, between all the haze and confusion of being a doctor for the first time, I tried practicing medicine.

Due to feeling completely overwhelmed however, I have scant recollections to share.

I stood scared every Monday morning during ICU rounds, as super intelligent pulmonary specialists grilled us mercilessly about the patients under their care, the diseases, the ventilator settings, etc. But first, they usually shared some joke or morsel of medical knowledge to try to relax us enough so that our jaws worked.

"Who here has heard of Koro syndrome?"

Nobody.

"It's the extreme anxiety, mostly in Eastern Asia, concerned with your penis retracting back into your abdomen and killing you. Some men sleep with their penis tied to the wall. Relax Dr. Lawrence."

Maybe the pulmonologist thought I looked so scared during rounds that he thought my penis might actually retract that far and kill me on the spot?

"And Dr. Lawrence, you wouldn't want to confuse Koro syndrome with a Candiru, would you?"

"No."

"And why not?"

"Because I've never heard of either one."

"Fair answer. Candiru, the fish that swims up your urethra when you swim in lakes in the Amazon."

Beyond treating us to tasty medical tidbits, the ICU doctors also expected us to take care of patients. I walked into the room of an assigned patient I had never met and read a recent report that diagnosed him with amyloidosis in his pericardium. We both looked at each other, a bit confused, wondering what to do about it.

I knew amyloid was an abnormal protein that causes problems when it is deposited in a patient's heart, in fact, I think I recalled learning that patients would die of this nasty complication. I knew he would need a cardiologist to deal with this issue and did not think it was my place to tell him that based on a vague recollection from medical school, I thought he was in bad shape. So, my involvement felt rather meaningless.

I watched a family's 29-year-old girl take her last breath. I took care of that woman for weeks—had spent hours at her bedside, conferred with her parents every day, took care of her after surgeries, sepsis, pneumonia, you name it. She fought it all and died. With each recurring admission that month, we knew she would die soon, but we kept managing to keep her going a little bit longer.

Despite her list of longstanding health issues, I thought we would somehow save her. How could you emotionally connect with a patient, laugh with her every morning, and think otherwise? I had to believe we were doing something worthwhile to alter the course of her life. That was what doctors were supposed to do, make her better. But we didn't.

It was another lesson: we couldn't save everyone. She had been stricken with a host of congenital issues and auto-immune diseases that left her system weakened with heart, lung, and kidney problems throughout her lifetime. No matter what was done to treat her, she kept coming back to the hospital and the medical teams kept doing everything possible to prolong her life. Before one last surgery, she had asked me for my opinion about going through with it and facing the recovery. I told her it was her decision, but with the possibility of fixing some of her issues, it seemed like the right thing to do. Maybe I was the only one with delusions that she would be cured.

She died several days after the surgery. I stood comforting her parents, thinking, the art of medicine people are right, it's an honor to care for these patients.

Later that month I was given a spreadsheet of the billing charges for all the patients I had cared for in the hospital. That woman's fees exceeded $350,000—that's a lot of caring and kudos to the art of accounting for a woman we all knew was not going to survive. Another elderly cardiac patient who went on to die had a bill exceeding $125,000 for his short stay with us. Again, a stay that we knew was ending in his death.

The patients that died seemed to have the highest bills by far. Our health care dollars appeared to be spent on prolonging life; a majority of billing largely spent on end-of-life care. I don't know how you quantify a human life, but we fought the hardest, and spent the most money, keeping people alive in a hospital bed or reclining chair for a few more days or weeks; some whose lives were fulfilled, some who had lived out their years, and all whose chance of survival we knew to be almost non-existent.

Death continues to hold a perfect record against human life.

THE WORK ROUTINE ON OUR FAMILY PRACTICE SERVICE WAS THE same as during medical school: Go see your patients early in the morning; write notes; be on time to discuss them in morning rounds (yuck); carry out patient orders, admit new patients, discharge healthy patients—all of which added up to several volumes of paperwork.

You probably noticed only "morning rounds" (yuck) earned some commentary, and it's strange to explain why I disliked it so much. Most likely due to what occurred at the start of rounds:

before heading out as a group to see our patients, the residents, students, interns, and our boss (the attending physician) would gather to discuss all the patients assigned to our team.

This critical daily meeting provided an up-close look, with no place to hide, directly into my confusion and lack of confidence as a doctor. And maybe I was just scarred from morning rounds during my first clinical rotation as a medical student where I left no doubt in anyone's mind that I was, regardless of dealing with lingering head trauma, the single worst presenter of hospital patients in the history of medicine.

A quick note on the term "rounds" as it does get used frequently and with slightly different meanings.

1. Rounds. When a doctor, medical student, resident, etc. says, "I have to *round* on my patients early tomorrow morning," they are referring to walking a*round* the hospital and visiting each patient they are responsible for in their hospital rooms.

2. Morning Rounds. Different services have different ways of handling morning rounds, but the general term refers to the entire team gathering *after* the patients have all been seen by the residents. With some groups, morning rounds occur while walking around from room to room and discussing each patient in depth after the patient is presented to the team by the medical student or resident. This was not a formal announcement such as, "Might I introduce Lord Mountbatten who has a tummy ache," but a formal explanation of what was happening medically to the patient.

3. Grand Rounds. Residency programs often have a required conference where a professor or resident presents a large learning topic for the week. Often a place to nap as a medical student.

On our family practice service, morning rounds took place in a small conference room on the fourth floor of our decrepit hospital. The patients admitted into the hospital overnight were discussed in depth. Plans were solidified for their care, collective minds scouring their brains—prompted by the omnipotent and caring attending—to construct the best possible treatment for the patient's physical, mental, and psycho-social well-being. These were intellectually stimulating conferences designed to enhance our learning of how best to care for patients.

I detested morning rounds.

Mostly, patients were discussed with the utmost regard for their dignity; but the next time you're slaphappy from being awake for twenty-eight hours, try politely deadpanning a patient presentation such as, "The patient was admitted to the hospital with a chief complaint that dragons were flying out of his butt." (True case, to be discussed later).

Morning rounds, the cornerstone of modern medical teaching, provided yet another opportunity to interrogate medical students and interns with questions, i.e. teaching by intimidation. In fact, when you interviewed for residency programs, the program directors all wanted you to sit in and visit their morning rounds, as if to say, "Look at all the crap you'll put up with if you join us."

Then again, perhaps sending me to morning rounds was their subtle attempt to dissuade me from even applying to their programs, while all the really promising candidates were taken out for sushi?

Our Family Practice morning rounds would start with a focus on one patient. The idea was for the team to go through the proper mental process of deducing what was wrong with the patient as though we were seeing him or her for the first time. We were to solve the patient riddle by asking questions about the history of what happened, asking about the physical exam, ordering lab tests we would want, and then deciding how to the patient appropriately.

We discussed the same types of cases over and over, ad nausea. Sound redundant? Exactly. That way, after talking in depth about how to treat a gastrointestinal bleed 213 times during rounds, when it was 4 a.m., and an actual patient was in the ER, bleeding out from their rectum, you would, instead of running down the hall and hiding in a closet, hopefully remember the appropriate medical protocol. Without thinking, you would reflexively order two large bore IVs, type and cross blood, order appropriate labs (Complete Blood count, blood clotting factors), call for help, etc.

You would learn which questions might be important to ask and which might be ridiculous and unnecessary: No need to worry about hobbies and sexual history, but asking if they were on a prescription of Coumadin (rat poison), which stopped blood from coagulating, might be critical as you determined where the bleeding was coming from, how active it was, how emergently the patient might need a blood transfusion, and how to reverse the problem.

You might be thinking, *why would anyone be prescribed rat poison?* Good question. Usually, to prevent blood clots from developing in patients with a prior history of blood clots, or in patients with atrial fibrillation, a heart rhythm that potentially allows blood clots to form inside the heart.

For all the cases of GI bleeding, of people showing up to complain about blood from their rectum, I would guess close to 99% were non-emergent, likely hemorrhoids causing a few drops of blood to make the toilet bowl look like they were starring in a horror film. But you could not be too relaxed, even knowing that most cases were not serious, because more than 15,000 people die every year from bleeding in their GI tract caused by taking NSAIDS (non-steroidal anti-inflammatory drugs, such as ibuprofen). So, when someone walked into the ER complaining of bright red blood from their rectum, they got everyone's attention very quickly.

Usually bright red blood signified that it was coming from the lower GI tract (the large intestines) because blood normally turned black if it passed through the whole tract from the stomach and through the small intestine—unless the bleeding was so rapid, let's say from a perforated stomach ulcer, that it was still red upon leaving the body; then you had a serious problem, hence the need to rapidly figure out what was going on.

You get the point, there were cases that demanded efficient reflexive thinking; and while protocols were designed to help you, it was during morning rounds where we could discuss the diagnosis and treatment protocols under relaxed (compared to the real event) circumstances where an intern's ego, and not a patient's life, were at risk.

And I leave you with this pearl of wisdom regarding intestinal bleeding: When a patient calls and says, "I just looked at my poop, and it's black. My poop is black! I googled black poop, and it says I'm bleeding from the inside."

One of the first questions to ask is: "Did you recently take Pepto-Bismol?"

"Why yes, I did, last night."

Pepto-Bismol turns people's bowel movements black—and often their tongue as well, so it's also a good question to ask when concerned patients call because their tongue is turning black, and they think they've caught the Plague.

Over and over, we discussed the process for working through the correct questions to ask, the correct labs and medicines to order for patients with hyponatremia, pancreatitis, pneumonia, cellulitis, anemia, congestive heart failure, diabetic ketoacidosis, heart attacks, colitis, and the very common "train-wreck" of an elderly person where nothing worked.

After discussing all the new patients admitted overnight, we would take turns giving detailed presentations on each of the patients whose care we were responsible for in the hospital. We followed this stimulating chat with a lesson on a pertinent medical topic, and then dispersed to complete the morning's work: mostly writing more orders based upon what was discussed in rounds (discharge orders, medication orders, lab or radiology study orders); tracking down lab and radiology reports; or re-visiting patients to ask the relevant questions that morning rounds had made clear I had forgotten to ask.

During those first months, afraid of missing any crucial information that would kill our patients, we tended to follow medical school training and ask patients every single question under the sun relating to health care. Granted, a patient with a skin infection might wonder why they were being asked about their sexuality, recent travel history, or any recent change in their bowel habits, but we were taught to be thorough.

Very quickly, however, we learned that the one thing *not* to do was find anything extra to discuss with a patient. With four patients waiting to be admitted to the hospital, seven hours' worth of paperwork to catch up on, a backlog of dictations, a presentation to prepare for morning rounds, the radiology department to visit in the basement, a nurse from the ICU demanding you immediately come evaluate a patient with chest pain, the cafeteria closing in six minutes, and time still limited to 24 hours in the day, you needed to move along.

If you asked every patient a question such as, "Have you ever been fatigued?" you'd typically get a ten-minute account of his or her bouts of fatigue over the last decade. As a result, it would take three days to admit your patients; not to mention, you'd miss dinner and piss off the ICU nurse.

Inevitably, the chance of someone answering "yes" to such a broad question *(who hasn't been fatigued at some point in their life?)* was directly proportional to how far behind you were on your schedule that day. Never mind that you would now be obligated to address a brand-new problem that probably had nothing to do with why the patient was even in the hospital.

Reading that last statement just caused the eyeballs of my past attending physicians to bulge, their sphincters to painfully cringe, and their neurons to burn with a desire to throttle me. Why? Because they dedicated themselves to training us to be good doctors, and being a good doctor included treating the patient completely while we had them in our hospital clutches. But I will remind you once more, there were still only 24 hours in the day.

Regardless of my desire not to add to my work, residents were responsible for going through a lot of questions with every patient we admitted. To speed up the process, the art of medicine people instructed us to tell the patient, "OK, I now have some 'yes or no' - type questions. Just answer 'yes' or 'no' to the following questions, OK? You got it? Yes or No."

"Yes."

"Perfect. Yes or no, has your appetite changed?"

The patient would then carefully think through the question, and which of the two answers she should correctly choose for a bonus prize. "Well, I usually enjoy egg salad with Aunt Myra on Tuesdays, but she went to church last week, so I didn't have my usual lunch. I ate more at supper, half a boiled egg. Myra makes wonderful egg salad. You look healthy, do you eat eggs?"

In this instance, I wanted to cry. But, after staring at the ground for a few moments, I took a deep breath, decided to move forward with my list of questions and committed the terrible mistake of accidentally letting the words, "Have you ever been fatigued?" slip out. I quickly tried recovering with: *"Yes or no only! Please!"*

"I usually have so much energy but lately, instead of my usual walk around the block, I turn back around halfway there, and find I am tired."

"Technically going the same distance, right?"

"What?"

"Sorry, was that a yes or a no on the fatigue?"

"I'm not sure. Do I look fatigued?"

Yet another verbatim patient encounter.

Efficiently practicing medicine the way we had been instructed was utterly hopeless.

The same complex formula of questioning applied with every single patient. The further behind you were in your work, and the sooner the cafeteria closed, the longer the diatribe would be regarding indigestion after eating liver and onions at a favorite diner. And while the patient was discussing the diner's ownership change back in 1952, I'd be left wondering what part of "yes or no"

I had yet again failed to properly convey, that had caused me to miss yet another cafeteria meal. Given that I was the constant factor in the failing doctor/patient communication equation, it was therefore likely that my education, which included studying English in college, must have been wasted. I seemed unable to properly express the simplest of requests in my native tongue.

On a side note, as you are certainly concerned with my missing so many meals, cafeteria workers often let us sneak into the kitchen after it was closed and grab anything left over. Our other source of food required letting yourself into the "physician's lounge."

An intense and undecided debate existed on whether medical residents were allowed into the hospital's physician's lounge. Physicians are doctors. We were doctors. That was my logical, courtroom-winning, inner dialogue, whenever I snuck inside to grab a snack.

But to the real doctors, we were whipping boys, not yet compatriots admissible to this sacred "lounge." The lounge had a television with several cable channels and the day's newspapers. A tray of doughnuts, bagels, and juice appeared in the morning, followed by a tray of cookies and doughnuts in the afternoon. If you were lucky, several doughnut scraps had been overlooked and some juice was left in the refrigerator. We survived on crumbs.

EACH OF US ON THE FAMILY PRACTICE SERVICE TOOK TURNS BEING on call every third or fourth night. When you were on call, you were responsible for admitting patients from the ER—or directly from a doctor's office—to the hospital floors.

During my first two years as a resident, I believed the ER was conspiring to drive me insane. Being paged to the ER was a personal assault on my health, a hospital plot to break my spirit. When your pager rang, and you saw the ER number light up, you knew you were about to be assigned a few more hours of work to add to your already high mountain of labor, and the more patients you admitted on call, the more patients you had to care for until they were sent home or transferred elsewhere.

I know, it was a privilege to care for these people—this was after all the job I had signed up for (without reading the job description too carefully), but the burden of having lots of patients meant that many more to examine, that many more notes to write, labs to follow up, orders to write, etc.

I admit I am being very whiny. But I was convinced the ER and residency program had placed cameras in our call room and waited until we were several minutes into any resting pose before they dialed our pagers. The resulting shrieking alarm convulsed me back into consciousness as I tried to grab the object of my disdain (the pager), resisting the urge to hurl it against a wall.

I had two revelations later in residency: first, after not seeing any of the supposed surveillance units in the ER, I began to think I had been merely paranoid, it was not really a personal attack by the ER to ruin a resident's chances of sleeping—that was the nurse's raison d'etre. Secondly, when I changed the alert tone on my pager from "screeching cat" to "relaxed bliss," I had a much more placid, and less pissed-off, frenzied tone when answering my pages. And just maybe it had required all of us surviving the intern year workload to eventually feel more relaxed and confident in our slowly evolving medical skills and abilities.

CLINIC LIFE

WHERE I SET RECORDS FALLING BEHIND MY SCHEDULE

Along with toiling on hospital rotations, we were also scheduled to work in our family practice clinic seeing patients several afternoons a week. These were our very own patients, patients who now considered us to be their family doctor. This clinic time was intended to reflect a normal Family Practice doctor's work experience.

My clinic, however, was not at all representative of a typical family practice clinic. Why not? Because of the two primary sources of patients who filled our schedule:

1) Patients passed to us from senior residents and attending physicians. These were the patients they never wanted to see on their schedules ever again because they had multiple frustrating, difficult and complicated medical issues you would never solve. They were what the senior residents and attendings termed "train wrecks."

2) The second source of patients for the interns was the nearby University hospital. When patients are discharged from a hospital they are instructed to follow up with a doctor. We became that doctor for hospital patients needing rapid follow up care.

A *typical* family practice patient usually comes in for a cold or to discuss a single, relatively simple problem, such as checking to see if their blood pressure medicine was working. The average person discharged from the hospital, however, was complicated and required extra work. The fact that they had recently been hospitalized inherently implied that they had some recent serious illness or medical issue. Furthermore, to care for them properly, we needed to call the hospital and request their medical chart, which then required time to read and understand why they had been admitted to the hospital, how they had been treated, and what was expected of us for their follow up care. As if, chronically running behind schedule, we had time to spare.

As an intern, brand new to the clinic, our patients therefore, far from being typical cases, were mostly very complicated, often mere hours from being sick enough to be hospitalized, all of whom required extra time to provide a minimum of care. Makes sense to give the newest, most inexperienced doctors, the most problematic and time-consuming cases, right?

Very rarely a patient checked in for a straightforward physical exam or annual check-up; in those instances, I stood shocked, uncertain what to do, repeatedly asking: "Seriously, you mean, you're just here to check about your health? You're not sick with multiple diseases and addicted to pain pills, anxiety meds, and anti-depressants?"

As an intern, we examined our patients and were then required to discuss their cases with an attending. The attending physician would quiz me about my patient and my plan for their care. During these sessions I inevitably discovered that the one scrap of information I had forgotten to ask the patient was the only fact the attending wanted to know.

The attending physicians must have been wondering what I was doing as I never seemed to have the pertinent information they demanded. At first their insight into what I missed during an exam felt mildly acceptable as they were present to teach us to be better doctors.

"I've just seen a twenty-seven-year-old male patient, here for a sore throat that started two days ago, mild subjective fever, no cough, no shortness of breath, mild sinus congestion, no sinus pain. Exam is unremarkable except for a red throat and red, swollen tonsils. I ordered a strep test...."

"Did you ask about his sexual history?"

"Uh, no."

Attending's eyebrows would rise, signifying utter disappointment.

"Why? Should I?" I innocently inquire, unsure of the association.

"What if it's gonorrhea causing the infection?"

"I think it's a cold... or maybe strep—"

"Go. Go ask."

I scuttled back to the patient, who was waiting for me to hand over a prescription of antibiotics, and instead, I would confuse them with a sexual history quiz that left them wondering if it turned me on.

It didn't.

At all.

Ever.

The strep test would be positive and the attending would shrug, "Our job is to be thorough."

After a while, however, the situation almost became comical. No matter how well I thought I interrogated a patient, and then presented their medical case, the attending physicians somehow guessed the one question I had left out.

"This is a fifty-two-year-old patient with a chief complaint of—"

"Did you ask about fatigue?"

"Um..I don't think so? Can I tell you why she's here first?"

"Always ask about fatigue."

"Ok," *I said, but did not completely agree with the statement. Why? Because as I already mentioned, everyone experiences fatigue, at least in my world, and if I ask everyone about fatigue, I'll make more work for myself, which was not an intern's goal.*

"Could be a thyroid issue. Always ask," the attending explained.

"Ok. But she's here for abdominal pain."

"Thyroid issues present in odd ways."

I'd go back down the hall, ask about fatigue, then return to the attending's office, but before I opened my mouth --

"Did you ask about family history of depression?"

"No."

Attending raises eyebrow yet again...and I promptly trot back to delve deeper into topics that wasted all our time, and supposedly taught us to think thoroughly and outside the box.

I'd return, "No, no family history."

"How about recent trips to Southeast Asia or dining at a sushi restaurant?"

"Really?"

"Could be parasites."

I swear they had planted microphones in the rooms and listened in for what minute detail I had left out; there was no shortage of room to show off my inadequacy.

But as I mentioned, our patients were not run-of-the-mill family practice cases. Then again, treating every other relatively healthy patient after those years was a breeze—so maybe there was some method to the madness?

As WE PROGRESSED INTO OUR SECOND AND THIRD YEARS, WE WERE expected to see a higher volume of patients. We could do this because our efficiency had improved, i.e., we'd learned what questions were useless and what parts of the exam you could skip. I am being slightly facetious, as you also learned to be more directed in your entire exam. But it was difficult to accomplish all that we were asked with each patient in terms of a lengthy interview and physical exam, then talk with our advisor, write prescriptions, discuss the plan with the patient, write a note on their care plan… rinse, repeat, and not be several hours behind schedule. The medical model was a nasty beast.

On one hand, the instructive attending physicians wanted us to be extremely thorough; and on the other, greedier hand, the hospital administration wanted us to see more patients.

At one point, to boost my sense of incompetence, I was advised that I was not seeing enough patients to generate sufficient revenue to survive as a doctor when I graduated. I left that meeting shocked and scared, accepting a brutal reality that I would complete residency and need a second job just to subsist.

I stumbled to my car, brainstorming about part-time jobs I could apply for just to eat and pay off student loans once I became a full-fledged physician. It was a really crummy sensation, knowing I had sacrificed that many years, signed on a mountain of student loan debt, all so I could work a full-time job unsuccessfully asking people to answer simple yes or no questions, and would then need to spend my evenings and weekends asking people if they wanted salad or fries with their order, just to pay off the privilege of treating patients.

I was seriously depressed after that meeting, and sat in my car for almost an hour, shocked, staring blankly out the windshield, wondering what the hell I had done to my life.

That was in my second year, and at the time I felt I was busting my ass seeing as many patients as was possible, staying late to finish chart notes every day.

When the averages came out for how many patients each resident was seeing per clinic day, my average patient number was higher than all but one third-year resident. My numbers were close to the attending level. Why the attending physicians felt it necessary to inflict that level of mental strain is baffling. Even though I made it a point to smile through my entire medical training as best I could, I felt terribly stressed on a consistent basis, and I'm not sure introducing more fear into our training provided any positive motivation.

One thing I learned however, was that even my bosses, the leaders of the residency program, were just human too. When I took over patients who had been under the care of one of the most compassionate Family Practice attending physicians, one of the "art of medicine" gurus, I discovered almost all of his patients were so completely gorked out on such whopping combinations of pain medications, sleeping pills, and anti-depressants, that I was not sure how any of them were still breathing.

Which was beyond hypocritical because the same doctor was one of our bosses who preached to us about not over-prescribing medications, especially not controlled substances. Looking back, I think he was either heavily invested in pharmaceutical stocks or just wanted to keep his patients comatose and not on his schedule.

It was, and still is, hard to find the balance between what was preached as good medicine—such as not putting people on antibiotics when they did not need them, not using anti-depressants or sleeping pills except for appropriate reasons and time frames, taking time to find out what lay at the root of the patient's problems—and what was practical. But this doctor, one of the heads of the residency program, who preached the art of medicine, who lectured us about monitoring for addiction and never over-prescribing controlled substances, was over-prescribing medications to every single one of his patients...and they *loved* him for it. They wanted a caring doctor to help them, which meant giving them medicine to fix their problems.

The vast majority of people did not want to pay a $60 co-pay to have an inexperienced resident doctor tell them they needed to try adding some yoga or meditation to treat their anxiety, and that maybe there was an emotional cause to their back pain—or just perhaps, weighing in at over 300 pounds on a 5'2" frame was not helping their knee pain; or maybe some walking would get their blood flowing and give them some energy. I'm not saying prescription medications don't have a place, they do, but people can also take a modicum of accountability to try some other solutions to at least help mitigate their problems.

But no, the patients had paid for something to be fixed and damn it, that meant pills. Pills, please! I once told a patient that he should incorporate physical therapy, yoga, and stretching into his day to help his chronic back pain. This was a very nice guy in his 50s. He was very receptive to these ideas as his next option was surgery.

I took time to find a good physical therapist that would accept Medicaid to help treat his back pain. He assured me that he had not received any pain medications in over two years, that he was excited to try physical therapy and was willing to do the exercises that I had gotten on my hands and knees to demonstrate for him in the clinic. He then asked me for a prescription for pain medication to get him through the next days. And because he seemed like a genuine guy, I wrote him that prescription. I explained that I could not refill the prescription as we were not a pain clinic; and he gratefully replied that he understood. I wished him good luck.

He showed up in the clinic two days later requesting some blood tests. That same morning, I had received a report showing that he was obtaining boatloads of different prescriptions for pain medications every month from several different doctors.

I listened to his story about a need for some blood tests and then he casually dropped in, "Oh, by the way, could you write another prescription for that medication that worked so well? You helped me sleep for the first time in two years, thank you so much. You're seriously the best doctor I've seen in years." (I'll get into how many red flags went flying with that statement in later chapters.)

I then read off the lengthy list of pain medications he had lied about not receiving.

He became furious and started yelling at me, "I have back pain and you suggest yoga and physical therapy? I can't afford physical therapy!"

"I found a place that accepts Medicaid. All you have to do is call and make an appointment," I reminded him.

"I don't have money for a phone call," he responded.

"I'll call for you right now," I countered.

"Are you going to give me my pain medications or not?" He asked.

"You're abusing them."

He followed my last response with a slew of impressive profanities and walked out cursing my existence.

Ah yes, the rewards of caring for people.

Despite my caring and compassionate attending physician's frequent reminders that I was overwhelmingly ignorant, I did make one great clinical diagnosis in that first month as an intern in the clinic.

A nice young Hispanic man came to see me because he had been feeling sick for the last few weeks and thought he had bronchitis. He worked as a bellboy in a hotel and had not been able to kick the cough for the last week. I agreed with him that he probably had bronchitis.

For some reason I had an intuition that I needed to do more testing than I would normally be concerned about for a mild cough and bronchitis. I asked this guy about his lifestyle (smoke that, my cynical attendings!) and found he was in a monogamous relationship with his boyfriend. I advised him it might be wise to do an HIV test, despite the monogamous relationship.

The following week in clinic, I saw the results of his test: HIV positive. Not only HIV positive, but with a very low CD4 count. His HIV had progressed to AIDS. Not good at all. There on my schedule for the afternoon was his name, the first patient I was to see that afternoon.

Right before I walked into the room, I remember stopping at the closed door and thinking, I am about to change this person's life—how do I do this? Walk in and casually announce it? Sit him down and offer it like the terrible condemnation it was? Be very clinical and just deliver the data and let him think about it?

What would the art of medicine recommend? A compassionate grunt and pat on the back? How would I want a horrible diagnosis delivered? I couldn't think of a good answer. There were no lessons to help at this point. I finally knocked, walked inside the room, and was introduced to his partner.

We all sat down, and I relayed the news. How well can you take being told you have HIV and AIDS? That's how well it went. There were tears and there were questions. I explained that we were going to get him referred to an amazing infectious disease doctor who specialized in HIV/AIDS. His partner held him in a tight embrace, both crying.

Going into the medical field, you know there will be bad diagnoses, sad outcomes, and difficult news to deliver. I thought I handled the situation as well as I could be expected to. It wasn't easy. And over the years, it never got any easier.

THE FIRST HELLACIOUS MONTH OF FAMILY PRACTICE SERVICE WITH NO days off finally ended. I promptly purchased the ingredients for gin and tonics. At the time I had gone on a few dates with a fledgling actress. Within days she was back together with her Hollywood beau. Just another example of why acting would have been a better career choice—they were hanging out together poolside, and I was about to land on the labor and delivery deck to start an obstetrics rotation.

OBSTETRICS—BACK ON THE LABOR & DELIVERY DECK

THE CIRCLE OF LIFE CONTINUES

After zero days off for the month of July (I know, I'm still complaining), I woke up as the brand-new intern on obstetrics (OB). I was back on-call, spending yet another night in the hospital I felt I never left.

Over the following years, working on the OB deck at this hospital became one of my favorite rotations. The hours were long, but the physicians from various community OB groups, the labor and delivery nurses, and anesthesiology teams were both fun to work with (mostly), and willing to teach. And perhaps most exciting, family practice residents represented the entire resident team. There were no OB residents to take patients away from you —nor to turn to for help.

The labor and delivery nurses, with years of OB experience had perfected a generous balance of caring for the patients while also taking time to teach the residents. They were absolutely fine working without us, but to their credit, they invited us onto the labor and delivery deck as part of the team. And finally, obstetrics is usually enjoyable work—there is a mixture of intensity and joy in delivering newborns.

The daily routine was similar to medical student obstetric rotations at the larger University hospital: Start the day with postpartum checks on the new mothers (*Have you passed gas? How much are you bleeding vaginally?*); sit through a pseudo-morning rounds to discuss a relevant teaching topic with an attending (*What do you do if an expectant mother develops high blood pressure?*); and then we spent the rest of the day and night delivering babies, checking on the mothers who had delivered babies, and being the resident in charge of the newborn nursery.

It was up to one of us family practice residents to call the attending OB physicians and update them about their patient's labor status. They could then swoop in and deliver babies without having to sit around in the hospital. We were also in charge of keeping these doctors aware of any pending emergency situations.

Now, on this, my first day on the deck, one of my initial patients was a pregnant Mexican woman who arrived complaining of abdominal pain. She had already visited her usual medical clinic earlier that morning because she was concerned about the pain. The clinic told her that they were too busy to see her. She was turned away.

I apologize to all you lawyer types whose ears just exploded due to blaring alarm bells.

A term pregnant woman?

Complaining of abdominal pain??

Being told to go away???

Are you kidding me????

This woman, in the 39th week of her pregnancy (40 weeks being the typically accepted length of time considered "term" for when a woman delivers—so 39 weeks was essentially term), came to see us in the hospital because she was still experiencing the same abdominal pain. Now, term pregnant women do experience varying degrees of abdominal discomfort—not shocking when they're carrying an extra forty pounds in their stretched-out abdomen—but if they complain, they need to be evaluated.

A nurse, following protocols, took the woman into an exam room and placed monitors on the patient's rotund belly to measure any abdominal contractions, and more importantly, to evaluate the baby's heart rate.

The monitor, however, was unable to pick up the infant's heartbeat. An educational pearl: In the realm of medicine, the lack of heartbeat is usually considered quite bad. Occasionally a baby's heartbeat can be difficult to find with a monitor, so you need to get a more exact measurement device.

The radiologist on call was still in the hospital. He wheeled in a more sensitive ultrasound machine than the one we kept on the deck into the patient's exam room.

A few minutes later he strode out of the room and announced to all of us that the baby had been dead for two weeks. I recall this so clearly, he then exited the labor and delivery deck, all without once breaking stride, as if he had somewhere more important to be. He made that two-week deduction because the bones of the infant's skull already appeared to be decaying.

So, guess who was elected to explain the situation to the family? Yours truly, since I was the only "Spanish-speaking" person present—and believe me, it was shoddy Spanish at best, with a severely limited vocabulary (recall me miming on obstetrics as a medical student?). But it seemed more appropriate for me to try in pseudo-Spanish then to have a non-Spanish speaker play charades with this devastating announcement.

This was not at all the fun of delivering babies.

If you read *Playing Doctor: Part One,* you might recall that during medical school, on my very first day on OB, in a painful circle-of-life moment, I learned of the death of a dear friend. And here I was on the rotation that supposedly creates happy memories, once more feeling nauseatingly shocked at news that was a far cry from anything joyous.

. . .

I entered the room and met the warmest and most congenial of families—a young pregnant woman, her loving husband, and their two beautiful twin daughters, maybe seven years old.

I sat down and introduced myself. I then attempted to explain to the mother that her baby had died two weeks earlier.

I told her the pain she had experienced throughout the day, the same pain that had compelled her to go see her doctor (unsuccessfully) earlier in the day, was due to contractions as her body was now trying to deliver her dead baby.

I explained that we were going to help her through this terrible situation. I felt sick to my stomach delivering this news.

But the pregnant woman wouldn't listen to my explanation; she was in complete denial, insisting that the baby had been moving that morning. I re-explained, several times, that she was feeling movements caused by her contractions.

It should have been apparent that I, the medical expert (not really) who had assisted (sort of) on at least forty deliveries as a medical student, would know more about what was causing a woman's pain, than the mother who had personally delivered twins. But she continued to refute my explanations.

It dawned on me that she was probably feeling pangs of guilt, so I assured her, best I could, that she had done nothing to cause this miscarriage, and that none of this was her fault at all. It was a terrible and tragic occurrence. There had been no psychology courses in medical school that taught you how to break bad news properly, and I had not yet reached the *Art of Medicine's* pinnacle of medical compassion where I reflexively grunted and touched a patient's knee, but I assumed any woman would want to be reassured that she had done nothing to bring about this sad death.

Eventually the whole family was crying. I too was fighting back sympathetic tears, and finally left the room to telephone the on-call, high-risk OB doctor to discuss our plan to help induce the woman's labor. He agreed with the plan, and I gratuitously talked with the nurses about what medicines to order. I say gratuitously because they already knew the routine and what to do, far better than me.

A nurse placed a medicine called Cervidil inside the woman's cervix. Cervidil is a medicine used to help induce labor, as it relaxes the cervix (the opening to the uterus, which is tightly closed to keep the baby inside). Often, once the cervix is relaxed, the woman's labor is triggered to complete the delivery. We planned on waiting for twelve hours for the medicine to work. After that time, if necessary, we would inject a medicine that induced contractions to help get the baby out, as it now posed a serious health risk to the mother.

When it came time to deliver the baby, we would give the woman anesthetic medicine so that she did not have to physically experience the pain of delivering her dead child.

This was all a protocol-based plan used for similar situations requiring inducement of labor.

Minutes after the Cervidil was placed, however, our standard, protocol-based plan took a serious detour. The husband walked out of the room concerned that his wife was bleeding a little bit. None of us were immediately alarmed; a small amount of bleeding was common after Cervidil placement, due to its placement irritating the cervix. A nurse went to check on the woman.

Seconds later I heard a shout from the room: "Dr. Lawrence, quickly, you need to take a look!"

Labor and delivery nurses have seen every sort of craziness in the world of obstetrics. They are typically cool, calm, and nonplussed; so, to now hear concern in the voice of one of the most experienced nurses was a bit disquieting. I jumped up and went into the room where the patient was writhing in pain.

Blood soaked the bed sheets. Lots of blood.

HOLY SHIT was my only thought as I rushed out of the room, telling the nurses to get the patient ready to wheel into the operating room.

I immediately called back the high-risk OB doctor, who, thankfully, was quite relaxed, because I was not. It was my first night on-call, and I wasn't remembering too much obstetric training as my head started to spin with thoughts of this woman dying.

I hurriedly related the change in circumstances, and the doctor asked what I thought. *What I thought,* was that he should be rushing over here quickly, not asking me questions, as I obviously had no place working in a hospital. But I put forth a less-than-succinct assessment that involved the possibility of anything I could remember related to medical school obstetrics, abdominal pain, and bleeding, mostly concerned with a placental abruption. He agreed that an abruption was likely and told me to get her into the O.R.—which thankfully, I told him I had already ordered.

This was an emergency. He would be there in minutes. I think the fact that I had already asked the nurses to prepare the patient for immediate transport to the O.R. made up for my incoherent rambling.

The placenta attaches to the inside of the woman's uterus and connects to the infant via the umbilical cord. A placental abruption is a condition where the placenta, which is flooded with blood vessels to provide the baby with nutrients, shears away from the uterus. An abruption can be small and only cause minor problems, like abdominal pain. An abruption can also be large and cause not only a lot of pain, but also rapid blood loss from the mother and the baby; rapid blood loss that is potentially fatal to them both.

This pregnant woman was actively bleeding fast enough that blood was now filling the bed sheets. In most medical situations, even dire ones, doctors were supposed to put on a "Chuck Yeager"-style persona and maintain a calm demeanor. This case, however, was a true emergency, and warranted no such demeanor. We ran down the hall and into the O.R. for an emergency C-section, while I tried using my meager Spanish to explain to the terrified husband and wife what was happening.

In the O.R., the anesthesiologist quickly gave the patient a spinal to numb her from waist down and then we prepped (cleaned) her abdomen for the surgery.

The high-risk OB doctor arrived minutes later. We performed a very rapid C-section that was most notable for the lack of lighthearted banter that usually filled the O.R. during these procedures.

In utter silence, the doctor pulled out and cradled a very handsome baby boy that was turning a horrible shade of purple.

A baby boy that had probably been alive not too long ago. A boy that had certainly been alive earlier that morning when the mother visited her OB clinic in pain, seeking help, and had been turned away. Definitely not dead for two weeks.

Nobody said a word.

The OB doctor was the only one to eventually express his anger, and even that was a mumbled and disjointed reflection of grief and rage under his breath as we were still caring for the mother, "Wasn't dead…not this morning...what a beautiful boy… goddamn it…he wasn't dead…"

Would this have gone differently had they been English-speaking? We would never know. A family more savvy to the ways of the legal system would have had a massive lawsuit against the clinic. Dead children leave little room for defense, and certainly none in this case. But I was on my thirty-second day of being a doctor and felt a combination of relief that we had saved the mother's life, anger at how she had been treated that morning, and deep sadness for this family. I stepped away to let the attending doctor handle the fall-out that likely never happened.

So much for the joys of the OB rotation.

THE REST OF THE MONTH WENT SMOOTHLY COMPARED TO THAT FIRST night. I delivered babies, asked post-caesarian section mothers about their flatulence, and became quite accustomed to sleep deprivation. On the rare occasion of being let out of the hospital, we were supposed to rest and catch up on sleep. One brilliant night however, I was convinced by friends with normal sleep schedules to head to the local border town's casino. The only problem was that I had to be back at the hospital at 7 a.m. for a 24-hour shift.

So, I went.

As the morning hours crept closer, I was down around $300—pretty much all I had to my name besides credit card debt. Then a winning streak started—so I had to stay until I was ahead, which only took until 4 a.m. It appeared I would be heading into a call night without any sleep; but residency was teaching me that I operated fine without it.

I drank about a silo of coffee during the two-hour drive back to work, was dropped off at the hospital entrance with a terrible stomach ache, and was comfortably delivering babies at 7:30 a.m.

Nineteen hours later and I was still functioning perfectly well without a wink of sleep, waiting between a woman's legs for the placenta to deliver. I glanced at a clock, thinking, *it's already 2:30 in the morning and I'm doing great.*

Although my foot felt kind of wet.

Why's my foot wet?

I looked down. I was sitting with my foot inside the bucket of amniotic fluid, blood, and feces. OK, I was doing marginally well.

New rule: no more all-nighters before call nights.

The bane of this service however was not the lack of sleep, it was covering the neonatal nursery at night. On call nights and weekends, we covered the labor and delivery deck *and* the newborn nursery. It was therefore a rare and blessed moment to lay your head down for a short nap. And while the nursery nurses were, for the most part, completely competent, there existed two nurses who made it their personal goal to wreak havoc on the intern's lives. These two, nicknamed the "nightmare sisters" by the residents they had tortured over the previous years, waited until you started to relax and then dialed your pager.

The labor and delivery deck would be clear, nobody needing a cervical check, no patients in labor, and you had been sure to ask the nightmare sisters, face to face, "Is there anything at all you need me to do or check on right now because I'm going to try and lie down for a few minutes?"

And they would smile and say, "No, everything's fine, the nursery is clear. Get some rest." And as you headed to the OB call room with its uncomfortable single bed, they would smile wickedly. And when you were almost asleep, your pager blared its alarm. It was the nursery with an asinine question about some routine order.

They would ask a simple question about a situation that they could handle just fine, such as, "Baby Newman seems to be spitting up on Similac. Could we change him over to some other formula?"

And you would say, "Of course." And they would page you again, five minutes later, asking if you could come take a look at baby Newman who was still spitting food.

As an intern you did not say "No" to a nurse—at least I didn't have the courage to. Nurses had a lot more practical experience than me and they knew the patients much better than I did.

I would return to the nursery and observe the pink and smiling cherubic baby Newman who enjoyed spitting. I would review the daily chart, add up the numbers, and calculate that the kid had eaten 150% of what was needed for his daily caloric intake; he had pooped and peed record-winning volumes more than anyone else in the nursery; he had gained weight, and he was heading home in several hours. I glared at the nurse wondering why she was concerned. She would just shrug her shoulders and tell me I should do an evaluation for the spitting up.

So, I did.

By the time I finished examining the baby and assuring everyone that he was not lacking for nutrition, and that he would, in fact, at his current rate of consumption, exceed the gross weight of an aircraft carrier by the time he was two weeks old, a woman would have started into labor, and there it was—sleepless on the deck yet again.

A (SORT OF) GENERAL SURGERY ROTATION

GALLBLADDERS GONE WILD

With the flip of a calendar page, I transformed into a surgical intern. A true surgical internship is notorious for being not only the single toughest year of medical training, but also possibly the worst year of a surgeon's life—but that's for genuine surgical interns. The attending surgeons all knew we family practice residents were never going to be surgeons, and therefore didn't work us nearly as hard as real surgical interns.

The surgeons we were assigned to work with did mostly outpatient or uncomplicated surgeries. In the mornings, we evaluated the post-op patients at a civilized hour. We then assisted on the removal of gallbladders, appendixes, and varicose veins. Even our on-call expectations were low and taken from home. We were only asked to cover two weekends of call, and rumors circulated that nobody was ever actually called back to the hospital.

Apparently, I wasn't nobody, and karma, knowing my head-injured synapses were still saddened about missing a host of learning in medical school, deemed it necessary that I do make-up work.

On my first night of call I went home after a full day, tricked into believing the rumors of family practice residents never being called in. I dressed for a bike ride, walked out the door, and my pager rang its alarm. Had I learned anything about challenging the gods of call?

No, apparently not.

I headed back into the ICU to evaluate a patient we had operated on that morning who was now experiencing irregular heartbeats. I looked at his EKG and thought I recognized SVTs (supraventricular tachycardia), a rapid heart rhythm.

There were folk tales of how to stop these irregular heartbeats. One included dunking the patient's head into a bucket of ice water. The logistics of this technique, however entertaining, seemed difficult to pull off, as the patient was semi-comatose, and more importantly, I had no clue where to find a bucket in the ICU. Instead, I decided to try the "carotid massage technique" whereby you massaged the patient's carotid sinus—which I believed to be somewhere on their carotid vessel—which I knew was somewhere on the neck.

I rubbed his neck. Shockingly, at least to me, the heart rhythm normalized.

I wrote orders for some medicine that would keep his heart in a normal rhythm; and when the surgeon arrived, everything was well and stable, with orders written.

To which the surgeon said, "Usually you guys don't get called in, but thanks for coming. I guess we'll call you in from now on. Good work."

Good work young doctor John. This recognition of competence went completely against my credo of keeping low expectations. I didn't actually have a credo, but, if I did, I'm pretty sure it would not include me building a reputation for wanting to be called in more frequently to do doctor work; I still wanted to make movies.

The month had started out quite fortuitously in that regard. I had attended the Telluride Film Festival during my first weekend off, where I met a big name (in the indie film world) director who asked me to be in his next movie. I was trying to keep my dream of acting and writing alive, which, in terms of far-fetched goals at the time, was up there with my becoming pregnant.

I had my moments, sneaking out of the hospital while on call and showing up at auditions in my scrubs, perspiring that my pager would go off for a code as I spoke an exciting line like, *"OK. Maybe that was not such a good idea,"* (a real line, from a real movie I was in, albeit years later, but it's apropos for my decision to leave the hospital and wait for the cameras to roll. I would ignore my buzzing pager, sweating through the already anxiety-inducing audition, thinking, *this is not such a good idea,* then race back to the hospital).

For some reason my acting agent kept sending me out for roles as doctors. Despite being in training to play one in real life, I still looked like a pre-med college student, not a real-life doctor, and was only cast in the doctor role several times. One was in an independent film that none of you have seen—and neither have I. The other time was in a popular television show playing an anesthesiologist, and I argued with the onset nurse consultant about how to properly hold a mask over the patient's face. Never saw that episode either, too busy seeing patients.

I did have a good friend who would get me into REI photo shoots, which she helped produce for paper ads (that's how old I am), and those paychecks saved my ass multiple times when I was close to vomiting about not knowing how I was going to pay rent with my credit cards already maxed out. Those were the most stressful shoots. I would be asked if I was available on a certain afternoon, and I would say, "Yes, of course." Then I would ask permission for a few hours off, as I needed to pay rent; and inevitably the photo shoots went overtime. I would be waiting for them to take a few shots of me walking with a backpack with my pager ringing as my senior resident wondered why I was not back yet. I ignored the pages and got in a quite a bit of trouble.

When I was physically present in the hospital, most of what I did, beyond giving neck massages to ICU patients, was "assist" with the removal of gallbladders using laparoscopy. People's gallbladders became inflamed, infected, or sometimes cancerous. The four F's, the risk factors for developing gallbladder issues, were a medical pearl, now likely shamed out of existence: Fat, Female, Forties, and Family history.

Regardless of biases, if the gallbladder was causing trouble, out it went. Three small incisions were made in a patient's abdomen, gas was pumped inside to expand their belly like a balloon; a camera was put into one of the incisions to look around and find the inflamed gallbladder; and then operating tools went into the other incisions to cut it out and remove it. Pretty slick.

I put the word *assist* in parentheticals because the surgeons were perfectly fine to take out the gallbladders without a family practice resident standing by to answer questions such as, "What are the risk factors for gallbladder issues?"

Since it was unlikely that any of us family practitioners would stumble upon a patient in the parking lot needing an emergent cholecystectomy (gall bladder removal), what was the point of being on a surgical service?

Hmmm?

Ok, good to learn what to look for in future patients, and to know when they should be sent for a surgical consult; learning good surgical techniques for even small procedures like lump removals or suturing lacerations—you learned how to hold scalpels, cut and put things back together without damaging skin tissue; how to prep the skin properly for repairing lacerations; and how to tie suture knots with your hands (not using forceps to assist), which is a point of great pride with surgical residents. When you see surgeons sitting or walking, appearing to be conjuring up some type of Harry Potter spell with their hands, they are actually practicing tying suture thread into knots.

Apart from removing gallbladders, the doctors we worked with were also famous for their work with breast cancer—another area of concern that would be good to learn as a family doctor: how to properly examine patients for breast cancer. The general and plastic surgeon worked together to remove malignant breast tissue, and then insert a breast implant. One "benefit" afforded these patients was that insurance companies would pay for an implant in the second breast to make things aesthetically pleasing.

Breast implants were remarkable. I was amazed every time an enormous water balloon was stuffed through a small incision in the patient's chest. Once both breasts had implants in place, the comatose patient was propped up and the entire OR staff, nurses, anesthesiologist, and doctors would stand back and stare at the patient's chest, trying to decide if her breasts were symmetrical. This constructive assessment of a woman's chest was done objectively and with complete respect; the patient was asleep and would certainly want her breasts to be evenly spaced on her chest. I will, however, add that I had begun to question if the patients were always fully asleep after a certain elderly patient, despite my repeatedly knocking her hand away, kept attempting to cop feels of my crotch while we were operating on her gallbladder.

Being on call was relatively enjoyable this month. Despite the misaligned decision to call me in more frequently, it was still home call. I had received multiple calls to come back in during the week but had only been called in once on the weekend, as the surgeons were graceful enough to give us some time off. So, one Saturday I thought I was safe to go to lunch with a blind date. My friends had set me up on several blind dates that had all been comically uncomfortable for everyone involved. Suffice it to say, there had been no second dates requested on either side. But this woman turned out to be quite lovely. She had tickets to the university's football game that afternoon and wanted to know if I could join her. I absolutely did. I don't really follow American Football, but I was perfectly willing to spend more time with this woman and learn to appreciate the game.

My call day was looking better and better as we sat at lunch and started discussing having cocktails and dinner after the game —and then I received a page to go to the hospital.

I was convinced that this attractive woman, a very cute reporter with a southern accent, was extremely impressed by my being called away from lunch to go save a life. Can you say Walter Mitty?

Meanwhile, back in reality, by the time I excused myself from lunch, she already had a new date lined up to go to the football game with her—some handsome jetfighter pilot who was apparently taking my seat at dinner as well.

I left the woman and scrubbed in for surgery, entering the OR just in time to help cut open the patient's belly. The stench of shit hit us all. This patient's appendix had ruptured and there was crap plastering his entire abdominal cavity. We flushed out his abdomen over and over to wash out all the feces. Hmmm, cleaning out splattered feces, or enjoying cocktails with a gorgeous woman? Residency was great.

During this month I had also decided to run my first marathon. I had not trained, but that never seemed to interfere with my medical work. In fact, I had only run ten times since the spring because of a ski accident (I coached young ski racers on the weekends and had crashed showing off for them in the half-pipe). After months of being in serious pain when I walked, I went to my pediatric orthopedic friend where an x-ray revealed I had cracked my pelvis. No wonder it hurt. So I had not really been able to run very much.

During this month of enjoyable, fantasy world, limited workload surgical rotation, I also started thinking about transferring to the surgical residency program.

When the surgeon I was working with found out about both the marathon and my thoughts regarding transferring to surgery, he shared this advice: "If you can go through the pain of running that marathon without training, then you can get through a surgical residency."

So, I ran. And it hurt. But I kept his words going through my head. At the halfway point, a man in a wheelchair was holding a sign that read, *"Pain is temporary, pride is forever."* I kept running, inspired by those words, until I saw my friends a few miles later, and promptly requested morphine (they didn't have any). I told them to never ever let me do something so stupid as running a marathon again.

But I kept running, swearing I would never do one again. Then I turned the final corner and was met by bleachers filled with people cheering. This was so much fun I was going to have to do it again—a total rush. I did not meet my sub-three-hour goal, but I finished close.

A few days later I received stellar reviews from the surgeons who advised me I was far more suited to surgery than family practice. But even I knew this surgery service had been a cakewalk compared to a real-life surgical residency—not even a cakewalk, more like comparing a beach vacation (albeit without the cute girl, because she was off watching football with some chiseled, jet-fighter dude who was taller than me, and had a real income), to a three-year prison sentence in the Gulag. But, for that very short time, I considered transferring to a surgical residency program.

You might rightfully question not only my considering surgery after such a friendly rotation, which was not at all representative of real surgical residency, but also, the amount of surgical training I received to be able to recognize surgical issues in my future medical career. Fear not, we had a second surgical rotation to look forward to for more teaching.

Residents were given the opportunity to go to Montana for the month and fly around in a private plane with a general surgeon, performing surgery in rural locations.

I did not go fly around Montana operating on the frontier, because, ironically, my future girlfriend, a surgeon, gave me a puppy for Christmas and he couldn't fit in the plane. Instead, I worked with another local surgeon who decided to invent a weird game whereby every day he altered his scheduled work location without telling me.

I spent most mornings trying to find which hospital or clinic he was working in; and if I found him, he was examining patients with hemorrhoid or gallbladder issues; besides which, by the time I found him, I usually had to leave to go work in my clinic.

Not a very helpful month surgically...the residents working with the surgeon in Montana were not expected to drive ten hours back to their clinic several times a week, but somehow, yours truly was not excused, and the residency program figured that if I was in town, and not flying the skies above Montana, then I had time to see patients in my clinic too.

Even worse, back in present reality, it was time to go back to the family practice service. And no, there was never a second date with the cute reporter.

FAMILY PRACTICE SERVICE: TAKE TWO

IF A PATIENT DIES, AND I DON'T PRONOUNCE IT, ARE THEY REALLY DEAD?

Time for Round Two on the inpatient medicine service, aka the Family Practice Service—the deplorable rotation that started my residency life with zero days off for the entire month. During those first weeks of being new interns, we'd been so slow to adapt to life as real doctors that we'd been unable to examine all our patients before sunset—which was inexcusable. So, our meager day or two off was rescinded to give us more time to work and learn how to be efficient. I didn't mind the work, but the decision to take away any days off had left me bitter towards the entire service.

This current go around on the same service however, promised an improvement over that first rotation because: 1) we had now experienced several months working as doctors; and 2) our team was led by an all-star Chief Resident who initiated the life-altering tradition of chiefs bringing coffee and bagels from the cafeteria for morning rounds.

The mere presence of baked goods immediately launched team morale to new heights. Just think, one bagel turned around my entire interest in medicine—imagine what a Belgian waffle might have inspired? I'm a cheap date.

I admit, morale on the family practice service had been shoved down into the tawdry hospital basement by my first experience, so any boost was appreciated; and now, newly inspired with carbohydrates, caffeine, and a friendly, instructive chief, I graciously accepted being back on the hospital's fourth floor and relinquished my overtly grumpy attitude.

This time around, knowing the rules and what was expected of us, we were no longer the newly dazed doctors in the headlights. Half the battle in the first months of residency was just figuring out what the hell you were supposed to do, beyond keeping the patients alive. Which unfortunately, didn't always work out—but give us a break, with less than a hundred days as doctors, we were improving, not perfect.

During the first week, one stunning medical complication on our team was the death of a woman who had just undergone hip surgery. If you're concerned that emboldened family practice residents were opportunistically performing hip surgeries, fear not; technically she had been under the care of the orthopedic surgeons because they had operated on her, not us. However, due to her being a diabetic patient with health concerns beyond sporting a shiny new hip, the surgeons had asked for our medicine team to cover her medical care—something they routinely do when patients have health issues beyond bony repairs.

Deciding who was truly in charge of a patient's care brings up something called *turf wars*.

Turf wars could be quite silly—deciding which medical team was in charge of a patient could possibly start Indian leg wrestling fights between different teams. Most surgical teams wanted complete control of the patient's orders and would be very upset if anyone countered their mandates. Other groups, like neurologists, were notorious for having one of our medical teams admit their patients at 3 a.m., and complete the evaluation and orders, i.e., doing all the work so that they did not have to get out of bed and do their job. Then the next morning, they sauntered into the hospital well-slept and fully caffeinated, ready to take over their patient's care.

Turf wars were a bit ridiculous (at least according to me, the doctor of ninety days), because it was usually quite apparent who should be responsible for the patient's care. The only legitimate discussions came about regarding super complicated patients, say, one whom the surgical, pulmonary, and oncology teams were all taking care of together. In those cases, occasionally deciding who should rightfully be in charge, with egos on the line, made some sense—and even then, there was typically an understanding of who was in charge. But mostly it was silly stuff that we were all accustomed to dealing with; that is, until we encountered the danger of turf wars.

The orthopedic team had repaired this elderly woman's broken hip (did a great job, too), and for the above reasons had requested that our service oversee her medical issues. (Side note reminder: "medical" issues, in doctor speak, means everything *not* surgically related.) So, the orthopedic surgeons would oversee all issues related to her surgery, and our family practice internal medicine team would manage issues like her diabetes.

When patients underwent hip surgery, and then dallied about on their back in a hospital bed not moving very much, they were at tremendous risk for developing large blood clots in their legs. These blood clots were the type that might potentially break loose, travel north into the patient's lungs (south if you're below the equator), and kill them suddenly—called a pulmonary embolism. Due to this potentially fatal complication, anyone undergoing hip surgery is placed on anticoagulation therapy—medication to prevent blood clots from forming in the first place. This was one of very few medical facts I actually knew.

How did I know this interesting fact? Another one of my *Slumdog Millionaire* moments: my first-year medical school class had an awesome intramural soccer team. We beat the university ski team (a national champion group of athletes), and the Norwegians (athletic Nordic skiers,) and everyone else we faced, indoors and outdoors. We medical geeks kicked ass on the soccer pitch.

During one game, however, I was kicked really hard in my shin, and developed an ugly massive purple bump on my leg. I did not think much of it until a bunch of fellow first-year medical students, experts that they were, convinced me that I had a blood clot forming in my leg, and that I must go see a doctor immediately because I was about to suffer instant death from a pulmonary embolism. Good chance that *"pulmonary embolism"* had appeared on the show *ER* that week and everyone was excited to pretend we existed in a fun, parallel drama.

Swayed by my classmate's concerns, I went to see a doctor and he scoffed at the pulmonary embolism idea, explaining that dangerous blood clots only happened in more serious situations like femur fractures and hip surgeries. I felt stupid for having wasted his time, but always remembered that blood clots and hip surgeries went together.

Back to the post-op patient: We showed up Monday morning for rounds to discuss the weekend's cases. Sadly, this patient had died suddenly the night before.

I actually raised my hand and asked a relevant question, "What was she on for anti-coagulation?"

The other intern flipped through all the patient's notes, looked through them several times, but could find no orders for anti-coagulation medicine.

It turned out that the newly deceased patient had never been started on any anticoagulation therapy and had suffered a pulmonary embolism because of the oversight on somebody's part —likely overseen due to both the orthopedic doctors, and our service, assuming each other's team had it covered in the orders.

Serious whoops.

Turf-wars 1: Medical Teams 0

I think most surgical teams would agree the onus in that case rested with the orthopedic surgeons; and had we been surgical residents there would have been a discussion at the weekly Morbidity & Mortality conference that would have left somebody crying for being an incompetent idiot. It was technically the orthopedic doctor's oversight, as they typically covered all the medicines to do with the surgery they had just performed. Even so, someone should have noticed the lack of anticoagulation orders typical for this surgery. It's almost a protocol-based set of post-op orders with checks and balances. Regardless, the woman died, and no lawsuit saw the light of day.

Point taken: turf wars can be stupid and dangerous.

Sudden death brings up a good time to discuss codes. It was on these inpatient rotations that we got to run codes—those moments when people, like that patient, had respiratory or heart failure, or collapsed in the hallway for unknown reasons—and we tried to keep them alive, or bring them back to life.

In those first months we had to quickly learn how to handle these codes, typically "code blue." Code blue referred to cardiac or respiratory arrest. There were other code colors, such as red for fire or smoke; black for bomb threat; pink for abducted child; green for mass trauma cases arriving—but mostly we were alerted to code blue.

Code blue situations were quite exciting. It was the closest we would ever get to acting like we were on television.

First, the code was called.

Either your pager alarm went off with a room number, or an overhead PA system announced, "Code blue ER, code blue ER," as in, the patient was turning blue in the ER. Then you ran down the hallway with the theme song from a medical TV show playing overhead (or maybe that was just in my head).

The major difference, however, one that *must* be understood, was that compared to running codes on fictional medical TV dramas—let's call it Fiction-meets-Reality Exception A; which is too long and truthfully, was more of a rule, so, let's change it to Rule A—was that the patients in real, life-threatening codes, usually died.

Actually, take it as more of a warning to anyone teetering on the code blue fence, so let's call it the Code B Caveat: code resuscitations usually fail, i.e. coding patients die—not always (fortunately)—but hospital-based codes with sick patients usually don't end well; so, coder beware, Code B Caveat, it's better not to code in the first place.

As I ran down the hall towards the code, I visualized the actors in *ER* running in slow motion, stethoscopes swinging—*that had to be what I looked like, a real doctor.* I smiled back at a family admiring me race to the announced code, and inevitably managed to smack myself with my stethoscope, or run into a doorway—maybe that's why they wear stethoscopes around their neck? And how come that tricky bit of reality, running with a stethoscope, an instrument designed much like a knight's mace or ninja's nunchuks, never makes it into medical dramas?

Which leads to a quick sidestep into hospital fashions. I am not sure who made the stethoscope around the neck fashionable, I assumed it was before *ER*, but you never know. Surgeons, as I have previously mentioned, never wore one around their neck, it had to be in their pockets. Eager medical students and internal medicine residents, however, wore it around their neck—perhaps signifying the noose the profession represented.

Meanwhile back to the code: Sprint down the hall and race to the patient's room where the code had been called. By which time one of the following situations had likely occurred:

1) Every single doctor in the hospital, and those who had been driving within a two-mile radius of the code, all with much more training than myself, had already arrived and the room was crowded, oxygen was low, and I was forced to peek in from the hallway, catching a glimpse of the unconscious patient's forearm.

As an intern you could now walk around offering people tea and biscuits while you waited to find out what happened.

And, most likely what happened was the patient died (Code B Caveat). Then everyone acted quickly to cover their ass, making certain that nothing had been done to cause the person to code in the first place, and that the newest code protocols had been correctly followed. The protocols changed quickly for a variety of reasons. For instance, a tropical shrub used to produce a conventional cardiac arrest drug was overused to the point of extinction, and we changed to a new drug, so everyone argued over which medicine to use—which rarely mattered because, referring back to the Code B Caveat, patients rarely survived these heart-stopping social gatherings anyway.

2) Code B Caveat, the patient was already dead before anyone arrived, and was not coming back.

3) I arrived in time to actually have a front row seat and be a player in the code where a mean-spirited nurse who never attended finishing school yelled at me, wondering who the hell I was, what I was doing and could I just get out of the way, or please go get something—and by the time I retrieved whatever she might have barked at me to go fetch...you guessed it, Code B Caveat, the patient was declared fully dead, not mostly dead (for you *Princess Bride* fans).

4) I could not find the code, which occurred almost as frequently as #5 below.

5) The code was resolved because the patient either got better or was never that sick to begin with. This situation was probably more common, thankfully, than the Code B Caveat. One of the best uses of the code system I heard about was when a resident could not get the pharmacy to deliver his patient's necessary medicine in a timely manner, so he pushed the code button, and got a lot of people to show up rather quickly, including the pharmacy carrying the patient's medicines.

Please note: not a lot of learning opportunities in the typical code situations mentioned above; not a lot to learn when you're peering above shoulders, or between legs, to catch a glimpse of how to run a code.

Most of the above situations occurred in the large university hospitals where everybody fought tooth and fist to be in on the code because they didn't happen frequently (which I suppose was good), so there was limited exposure to these important hands-on learning experiences. Also, in the larger hospital it was cool to say you were in on a code, so people scrapped and tussled to get in the room and be cool. Rule B, doctors like to do whatever makes them look "cool."

In the smaller hospital, where we were the only residents, most of the above situations still prevailed; however, during the nights and weekends there were significantly less people to crowd the rooms—which initially sounded like a good learning situation.

I slowly gained a comfortable level of proficiency in helping during codes. I had even discovered a polite way to move in on the hands-on work using Rule B to my advantage. Most doctors were slightly insecure. Their sub-conscious behavior was based on overcoming the traumatic years of being the science geek that was pummeled on the playground (except for orthopedic doctors, like gold medal speed skater Eric Heiden, he was probably never beaten up on the playground). The pillars of their psyche were focused on now doing whatever was supposed to be the coolest thing possible.

The other majority group in medicine, next to the precocious science geek, was that overachieving sport-jock, class-president type that already presumed they were doing whatever was cool anyway. Essentially playground class warfare still existed in a power struggle to see who really was the coolest person at recess (which is what a code was in a weird way, a break from the usual required tasks to get out and play heroic medicine)—so, Rule B was important.

Another tangential note, I didn't really fit in either group. I was the liberal-arts-educated student who had avoided being beaten up on the playground, avoided conflict in general, and was now hamstrung with serious imposter syndrome about what I was doing compared with these other people who were more obviously doctors.

Back to appearing cool and suave: The first doctor to arrive ran the code (i.e., gave orders), so that person must therefore be the coolest person present because the coolest thing to do was run the code. However, the hands-on stuff that made you appear to be the person saving a life is what *looked* cool. For instance, it looked *really cool* to be pumping life back into the patient's chest. The guy standing there performing chest compressions, perhaps the night janitor recalling his boy scout first-aid course, looked like a miracle worker yanking the patient back from the dead with his healing hands.

So the head doctor who was running the code usually demanded to start off doing chest compressions along with running the code. Why? Rule B, it looked cool. Most high-level doctors who knew what they were doing, however, were out of shape and slightly pudgy (Except orthopedic doctors, they were cool *and* rarely pudgy; and a lot of cardiologists who must have recognized firsthand that being slender was easier on their hearts), so they broke down in a sweat and became breathless rather quickly.

Did it look good to pass out in front of the nurses?

No.

Rule B: look cool.

So these close-to-fainting doctors covered their fitness inadequacies with frequent stops where they heaved out some comment like, "Let's see how he's doing." Then everyone stopped and looked at the monitor while he or she caught their breath.

The fact that the doctor was sweating profusely looked great. It appeared like we were all giving our best efforts to get the patient back to being sick in bed.

Meanwhile, despite the need for practicing codes, I did not think we wanted a second unconscious victim.

So, I learned to slide in with a respectful save, "Excuse me, sir, do you want me to take over the compressions so you can manage the code?"

Or "Do you want me to take over so you can place a line?"

Or, most subtle of all, "Do you want me to place a line?"

Going back to Rule B, doctors always wanted to place their own lines because it looked spectacular.

As soon as I offered to place a line, they responded with a reflexive, "Here, you take over the compressions, I'll place the line."

Please take a moment to admire my brilliant Machiavellian social climbing in a code situation.

What we are discussing are various ways I had to try and get myself code experience beyond playing cocktail waitress. Giving chest compressions was a good and safe place. First off, it looked cool, and that was what was important (Rule B). Then, if the victim survived, you were hoisted around the hospital ward on people's shoulders as they sang, *"For he's a jolly good fellow!"* (Actually, you just went back to work).

Secondly, if you were busy giving compressions, it was reasonably excusable to not be responsible for doing anything else in the code, like thinking. Giving compressions required forcefully compressing the patient's chest, not giving a sensual pectoral massage as they do on *Grey's Anatomy*—this was energetic and forceful work that could break ribs (the patients, not yours hopefully). It did not leave much room for people to pepper you with questions that could make you look stupid while you were busy counting the number of compressions.

Thirdly, you were up front, close, and personal with what was going on, so you could see firsthand how to handle a code. Knowing codes occurred infrequently, you might have correctly surmised that it was difficult to gain significant amounts of practice in an otherwise stressful hospital event.

How then to practice the art of saving lives when people went into arrest? Of course, we residents would have improved hospital experiences if patients coded more frequently. We should probably evaluate available (and legal) methods for putting more patients into cardiac arrest. Just kidding, but it does sound like a decent medical thriller plot.

A more reasonable suggestion was having medical students volunteer to go into cardiac-arrest or at least allowing us to treat them like arrest patients for extra credit—but that idea also seems unlikely to gain wide acceptance.

Instead, we had a life-size dummy on a table where we did simulations to recertify our ACLS licenses by passing *one (just one)* of many code possibilities—and that, with a lot of guidance. Were we under-prepared? Not if that exact code situation occurred while we were being coached what to do by an attending physician holding the guidebook next to us.

Otherwise, yes.

FIRST TIME PRONOUNCING DEATH:

There's something that happens in hospitals, people die. If you're unsure, refer to the Code B Caveat, people die. It happens. The emotions accompanying death deserve a chapter to themselves; but rarely talked about is what happens after someone dies: we pronounced them dead.

"Pronouncement" sounds like the town crier blew somber notes on his trumpet, unrolled a scroll, and read the announcement of death. I am guessing the whole pronouncement ritual was based upon formally ensuring that the person who died was truly dead, and not going to be put in the ground, or cremated, if they were still alive and merely feigning death to get rid of unwanted visitors, or perhaps avoid debt collectors.

I had heard the term, *pronouncing death,* but had received zero instruction as to what it entailed. So, the very first time I was sent to pronounce somebody's death, I had no idea what I was supposed to do.

It was a busy night, and I was in the ER admitting yet another patient to the hospital, when my pager buzzed; it was a fourth-floor nurse wondering when I was coming up to pronounce a woman's death. I had no clue what patient she was talking about, let alone the fact that the patient had apparently died. I told the nurse I would be up there as soon as I finished.

It was probably another hour until I was finally able to break away from admitting our ER patients to the hospital.

I asked my chief resident if there was anything special I was supposed to do, some magical pronouncement or test to perform, or paper to sign. Just walking in, looking at the body and declaring, "Looks dead to me" didn't seem appropriate.

The chief advised me, "Listen for a heartbeat, sounds of breathing, do some neurologic tests, and write a note saying they were all missing. Then get back down here, we have another patient to admit."

That didn't sound too tricky—and I wasn't expecting the now dead patient to critique my performance anyway.

I walked upstairs to the fourth floor, and into the room of an elderly patient whom I had never met, and never would in this world. Then I stopped abruptly, not expecting anyone else to be in the room. A woman I assumed to be the patient's daughter stood crying next to the bed where her mother lay. The deceased woman's mouth and eyes were held slightly open. Hours had passed since her last breath.

I introduced myself to the daughter, expressed my condolences, and explained that I needed to quickly examine her mother to officially pronounce her dead.

The daughter nodded and then held out something in her hand, "While you're here, could you please put these back in?"

I stared down at a set of dentures in her open palm, and tried to hide my revulsion, avoiding the instinct to jump back.

No idea why, but I've always harbored a nauseating aversion to dentures and retainers. More relevant than my irrational disgust however, I had never replaced anybody's false teeth, and had no idea if there was a special technique for inserting the large piece of plastic into a mouth, or for locking it into place.

I quickly improvised to cover my ignorance (and oddly placed revulsion), "Uh, that's something the funeral house usually does for you, to make sure it's done right. This will just take a second."

I turned around, bent over her mother's body, and listened for a non-existent heartbeat; I stared at her chest and saw no signs of breathing; I shined a light into her pupils, which elicited no reaction. She was either dead or faking it extremely well.

I decided to finish my job with a dramatic movie type gesture: softly closing both of her eyes with one hand, a gentle good-bye as we now officially confirmed that she was indeed dead. I let my hand rest for a second, a final farewell—then I started to step away.

But her eyes didn't stay closed; they just popped back open, staring at me. I tried closing them once more, and realized that with her having been dead for several hours, her body had somewhat stiffened, i.e. rigor mortis had set in.

So much for noble gestures.

I turned around to leave both women just as the newly arrived son-in-law walked into the room. He walked over to comfort his wife with an embrace. They exchanged a few words and he looked back to me. I introduced myself, once again expressing my condolences. I explained that I had completed my exam and would leave them in peace.

We shook hands. He grasped my hand firmly, and then proceeded to offer me the yucky- looking flesh-colored plastic and metal retainer with fake teeth in his other hand, politely requesting, "Would you mind putting this in while you're here?"

He was a tall, stately person with absolutely zero knowledge of my newly implemented hospital protocol for avoiding touching dentures.

"Uh, no… of course not," I slowly replied, looking to the wife to save me with her freshly acquired awareness that such jobs were handled in the funeral parlor; and we shouldn't go trampling on the funeral home's areas of expertise for fear of starting a somewhat macabre turf war.

Instead, she boorishly chose to just stand there weeping.

Reluctantly, I moved to my uncertain task. I turned my back to the couple, and leaned over the deceased woman yet again, determined to overcome my own ignorance to the workings of false teeth. They could only be so complicated. I decided to try just shoving them inside her mouth.

I became immediately re-acquainted with my previous obstacle, rigor mortis. The same rigor mortis that had already foiled my graceful eye-closing farewell, now held her mouth slightly ajar, but also clenched tight enough to not allow me to place the dentures all the way in her mouth.

I glanced over my shoulder to see the husband holding his crying wife, while he smiled down at me. I smiled back and returned to face this tight situation. With my back to the family members, I shielded any obvious effort as I attempted to wrench open the locked jaw, and jam the dentures in place—didn't work, the pressure spat them back at me.

I held the mouth open while trying to wiggle the dentures inside. They kind of seemed to stay in place—a little crookedly perhaps?

I looked over my shoulder once more. The dignified husband was still smiling, no expression of shocked repulsion on his face, so I turned back to check the dentures which, astonishingly, now sat, jutting outside her mouth with all the tension of her closing jaw, like two springs, about to shoot them into the air.

I quickly pushed them back in.

Her jaw shot them back out.

I shoved them back in, hard, heard something crack, and then pushed them even further inside.

I quickly turned around and headed for the door, explaining that I really needed to go.

I stepped into the hall, anticipating a champagne cork "pop" followed by startled screams of disgust as the dentures flew through the air and hit the floor. Instead, I overheard the husband say, "It's okay dear, I'm sure the funeral home people can do it properly."

MEANWHILE, DURING THIS RIVETING MONTH OF INPATIENT medicine, I was still seeing my clinic patients. This seems like a good month to discuss Reba. I bring up Reba because she was basically a walking version of my inpatient medicine patients. Reba represented the wonder of contemporary healthcare. A sweet woman who had smoked so much that by age 49 she looked not a day younger than 132.

Reba was on disability because she had developed a permanent lung condition that I never completely understood. I didn't understand the weird lung condition, and I certainly didn't understand why our taxes were being used to pay for Reba not to work since she was the one who had decided to smoke all those cigarettes in the first place.

The lung condition would remain a mystery to me because it had been diagnosed at the Mayo clinic. What does the Mayo clinic have to do with my not grasping her ailment? Because the Mayo clinic conjures up images of the brightest minds possible—minds unquestionably brighter than mine—unraveling complicated medical cases. So, when Reba told me she had a lung condition that had been diagnosed at the Mayo clinic, and that it was rare and difficult for even the Mayo clinic doctors to understand, I believed her.

Years later I noticed a pattern with that clinic so chock full of intelligent minds: apart from Reba, everyone else I knew that was sent there to finally diagnose a complicated medical condition came back after a week-long massive battery of tests without finalizing any conclusion—which might have been what they told Reba about her lungs, and she interpreted their lack of any specific diagnosis as her condition being too complicated to understand, but serious enough to require keeping her on disability. I'm sure they do great work, but that was what I noticed, lots of tests for inconclusive diagnoses.

What I did know was that the senior resident, the one who had cared for Reba during the previous three years, had apologized profusely when he passed her medical chart to me, thus relinquishing his care—and then he walked off into the sunset, laughing.

Reba not only suffered from her bizarre overly smoked lung condition, but also boasted uncontrolled diabetes and hypertension, was grossly overweight, and developed urinary tract infections every time she saw me. I had that unproven power.

Despite repeated mandates from both myself and her lung specialist that she needed to stop smoking, as it would eventually kill her, she continued to huff and puff through a minimum of three to four packs a day.

The complications of her various diseases landed her in the hospital every few months, and on my clinic schedule every week. And you and I paid for the complications of her smoking habits, paid for those hospital bills, her medications, and her frequent visits to yours truly.

She was a friendly woman who loved to talk and talk about anything but her health, which was not only a disaster, but also the reason you were paying for her to see me.

For months she told me she was good about drinking lots of

liquids, filling her ever-present, 96-ounce, gas-station drink bucket, several times a day. I eventually discovered, though my chief inspector-like questioning, that she did indeed fill her Enormo-mug several times a day—but with Dr. Pepper or Coca-Cola. These types of realizations, ones that broke over time, became topics of discussions that kept us from ever really discussing her lungs.

And to really keep me off-balance, Reba often brought her ex-husband, whose ribs she had broken, twice, with a frying pan. He looked like a caricature of Gomer Pyle with missing teeth. They still lived together despite being divorced. They had learned to play the system, and somehow received better disability benefits if they were not married.

I dreaded seeing her name on my schedule. I knew her visit would take no less than forty-five minutes, regardless of which, against my continuous requests to the front desk to increase the length of her appointment, they continually scheduled her for only fifteen-minute slots. Maybe it was just a game the front desk liked playing on interns. Reba and I would barely finish saying hello (which somehow took twenty minutes) before the front desk started yelling at me through the clinic room door that I was behind schedule and had angry patients waiting. Which did nothing to speed up Reba telling me about her lungs and left me wondering why nobody *listened to my request to schedule this woman for adequate time.*

Both she and her ex-husband appreciated my taking *so* much extra time with them (none of the other waiting patients did) that one day the husband piped up, "Hey, Doc, guess what? I'm gonna change my insurance so I can start seeing you too. You're gonna be my doctor!"

I tried smiling through suppressed tears and lied right to his missing teeth, "That's great, that's going to be a...just a great experience for us all. Thank you."

One of my great medical successes was finally getting Reba on anti-smoking medications, which helped her to actually cut down her smoking habit. Between anti-smoking medication and a replacement program involving her inhaling large bags of gummy bears (which really helped the diabetes), she cut out smoking altogether.

That pretend anti-smoking success lasted several visits until I learned she spent all her free time with friends inside a trailer-home inhaling second-hand smoke. She was smoking a week later, and back in the hospital being treated for pneumonia several days thereafter.

And who paid for that visit?

EMERGENCY ROOM

THE IDIOTS GUIDE TO FOOLING DOCTORS

Now, as the end of the millennium approached, many people began to fear an event called Y2K. As our Gregorian calendar approached the year 2000, computer clocks would reset to the year '00, and nobody knew if that zero-year denomination would trigger complete shut down and collapse all related systems. The world, running on the Internet and computers, might just stop, thereby triggering total global chaos. Meanwhile, I was about to start playing a real live doctor in the ER. I'm not sure which situation sounded more ominous.

I'll quickly break the tension and remind everyone that, thanks to people far smarter than me (likely a bunch of pre-teen computer wizards), Y2K never caused any issues—we're not sure if we can say the same about my time in the ER. I was excited to start emergency room work, and not just because *ER* continued to be the trendy television medical drama. Firstly, ER shifts were pretty entertaining compared to most other rotations. You handled a wide variety of patient's medical issues which kept you on your toes. You might be treating a laceration, a heart attack, and an injured shoulder, all at the same time. And most lovely of things for a resident, it was shift work. Once you finished your shift, you went home; you were done working, and did not have to do any call nights with thirty-six hours of work in a row. (Covid, the nasty bugger, has likely changed ER work to being a non-stop, round the clock, shift for ER teams).

(Bonus points to all of you who picked up that in my ER shift work excitement, I forgot all my art of medicine family practice training and referred to the patients as the pathologies to be treated, not as people.)

Practically speaking, ER work is good for inquisitive, passion-ate-to-learn-about-medicine, residents. Why? Because not only were you exposed to a wide variety of medical cases, but you also needed to think quickly, and even though not all of us would work in the ER, it created a great opportunity to learn which types of medical cases you could treat in an office, and which were best sent to the ER for treatment or hospital admittance. And, did I mention, *it was shift work. No being on call!*

On top of all these enjoyable reasons to spend time in the ER, it was also the place many people used as their primary medical facility, so it was an excellent place to work up patients without knowing much about their medical history. When you worked on the hospital floors, the patients were typically admitted with a diagnosis and you started appropriate protocol treatments, often without having to do much further workup (not always, but a lot of the time); whereas, when someone showed up in the ER with chest pain, you had to figure out if their pain was caused by a heart attack, pneumonia, gunshot wound, or indigestion—i.e. you had first crack at solving the mysteries, puzzles, and riddles of patient diagnoses before anyone else.

You've figured out the intern routine by now: go see patients, then present your findings to an attending physician who would green-light whatever plan you've come up with to care for the patient—or shoot down your shoddy idea, and hopefully instruct you to think about what you might be missing in a diagnosis or treatment. Once the ER bosses gained confidence in you (or lost it altogether), they let you act more (or in the latter case, less) independently. Fortunately, the ER doctors recognized me from my time admitting patients to the hospital floor, and knew I was relatively competent.

I was not, however, immediately let loose to start cracking chests open, removing bullets, or intubating the patients I decided needed help breathing. Partly because I needed to earn the right to care for the patients, but mostly because we didn't see a lot of bullet wounds or chests needing to be emergently cracked open.

Our hospital's ER was a level two-trauma center, so the big trauma cases went to the larger hospitals (level one-trauma centers), while we saw a mixture of other problems—some serious, and some serious to the patients.

My very first patient on my very first day in the ER was a young woman with a severe headache. When I entered the exam room, the lights were turned off because lights exacerbated her headache. The patient lay on the exam table moaning in pain. I spoke calmly and quietly to not make her head feel any worse, "Hi Nancy, my name's John, I'm one of the doctors here today. I understand you have a headache?"

She attempted a brief, small smile for my compassionate efforts, "I'm having the worst headache of my life...feels like a migraine, but worse...," her smile replaced by a grimace of obvious pain.

That phrase however, *worst headache of my life,* is a catchphrase that medical students have been trained to respond to like Pavlovian dogs, drooling with excitement (and in my case, fear), because they were the words patients typically used to describe the pain associated with a hemorrhage in their brain.

I did a rapid battery of physical exam tests, and quickly went to discuss this potentially fatal headache with the attending physician.

My attending for the day was a fantastic doctor and great guy:

always very relaxed and instructive, who appeared more likely to be crafting micro-brew in the ER office, while lecturing about existential philosophy in between poetry jams, than saving lives. I was very concerned about the patient and just blurted out, "I'd like to order a stat head CT to rule out a subarachnoid hemorrhage for this patient."

"Stat" sounded kind of cool to say in this, my virgin, and quite emergent, ER case.

The attending appeared nonplussed, awaiting further explanation without any reaction to my urgent use of the word "stat."

So, I blundered on, "This patient, Nancy Beckstead, twenty-seven-year-old woman, here with a chief complaint of a headache that she describes as... *(drumroll please) the worst headache of her life* (dramatic pause... but *still no reaction from the attending)*. Uh...the headache woke her early this morning..."

"Did you say Nancy Bankstead?"

"No. Beckstead."

"Nancy's a frequent flier here. Every Saturday. Just don't give her any narcotic drugs."

And then he went back to casually reading his newspaper.

What? I was shocked. My patient was probably going to die; I wasn't worried about pain meds—although, I did need a plan to treat her pain because, well, doctors are supposed to help relieve their patient's pain. But I still needed to figure out what to do.

"So, don't order that stat CT?" I asked.

The attending shook his head at either my silly re-use of the word *stat,* or more likely, my inability to grasp that Nancy was a big fat liar.

"No. Tell her to follow up with her doctor this week."

I sulked out of the office, while the carefree attending turned back to his bagel and morning newspaper, calmly calling out to the nurses' station, "Barbara, can you pull a recent DOPL on Miss. Bankstead?"

I returned to Nancy, tiptoeing back inside the dark, quiet room, and politely asked her what medicines she had used for headaches in the past that had helped. Amazingly, *all* of them happened to be narcotics—the exact same medications I had just been instructed *not* to give to her.

I suggested a non-narcotic pain medicine.

She was allergic to it.

I suggested a different non-narcotic pain reliever.

Remarkably, she turned out to be allergic to every single non-narcotic pain reliever ever available in the world. I told her about a brand-new pain medicine that did not have the opioid effect of narcotics—but she was allergic to that one too.

Amazing.

Turned out she was a complete medical anomaly, and allergic to every class of pain medication *except* narcotics. Now what was I going to do? She was in pain, and the only medicines that helped were narcotics.

We were in a serious conundrum. Fortunately, Nancy was quite helpful and forthcoming about telling me that she didn't even like taking pills, but in the past, when she absolutely needed something for pain, a medicine that she thought sounded something like, "*Perk-o-sot?*" had worked really well.

And regarding following up with her doctor, unfortunately, he was out of town all week, so her care, her wellbeing, her only chance of breaking the horrific migraine pain cycle, was left in my caring hands.

I returned to the attending's office to inform him of Nancy's allergies, and her doctor being out of town all week. My medical career was now reduced to playing messenger boy and patient envoy.

The attending tossed his newspaper aside, strode back to Nancy's room, flipped on the lights, and loudly announced, "Hi Nancy, we're not giving you any narcotics today. Anything else?"

She left the ER two minutes later walking upright, and not appearing to be in any pain.

I was *shocked*. She had barely been able to lift her head ten minutes before. *She had lied right to my face!*

The nurse then showed me a three-page long DOPL fax (**D**ivision of **O**ccupational and **P**rofessional **L**icensing) listing the variety of unwitting physicians from whom Nancy had received narcotics in the last month; there were many, but I didn't feel any better for joining the ranks of the duped. Always remember this pearl of wisdom: listen to the nurses and ask them about the patients. The ER nurses know the frequent fliers, and will quite often tell you, *before* you walk into a room, why a patient is *really* there.

So that was my first ever ER patient as a doctor: an unhappy patient I thought was dying, who was really just a naughty fibber wanting narcotics, and who stomped out without any treatment. She provided a lovely preview of the patients I could expect to see all month in the ER.

Many patients being evaluated in ERs around the country are people seeking pain medication. And some of them might be dealing with very real pain. But there exists an entire population of pain-medication-seeking people spending their days shopping between various emergency rooms and clinics, finding out who is willing to write them for highly addictive narcotic- or sedative-type drug prescriptions.

While there are certainly patients legitimately seeking pain relief, their plight is often ruined by the volume of people seeking recreational drug highs, tragically addicted to the medications, and not able (or willing) to find decent help to treat their addiction. There are also people making serious cash (and let's not delve into how much profit the pharmaceutical companies are churning out on narcotic addiction) selling narcotic and other controlled medications.

We all knew that there were quite a few entrepreneurs creating their living by selling controlled substances (narcotics or sedatives) on the street. They received a prescription from the ER for pills that they might use or sell. The ER visit and the prescriptions were paid for by insurance carriers, often Medicaid or Medicare. The pills might sell for 10 or 20 dollars each. Twenty pills (paid for by insurance, funded by those of us paying premiums and taxes) sold on the street for $20/pill=$400 profit. Meanwhile, I was scrounging for rent money and sneaking into the physician lounge to eat bagel scraps.

Maybe it was a just a game to these people. Apparently, there are quite sophisticated operations in organized crime worlds to receive cheap prescriptions for buckets of pain pills to be paid for by insurance carriers and then sold on the streets. And the abuse came from every socio-economic walk of life.

But I was a non-sophisticated newbie doctor, i.e. easy prey to narcotic seekers, and blind to the lack of headache being feigned in front of me. But I quickly learned the wily patterns of master drug seekers.

Their medical complaints were usually problems that were difficult to corroborate with objective findings, such as Nancy's headache. You were in for a long day if you chose to argue with people over whether they did, or did not really have a headache, as there was not yet any objective lab tests available to determine if a headache existed, or if the patient was just a really well-trained actor.

Kidney stone pain was another favorite scheme used in an attempt to fool doctors. Patients limped inside the ER, holding their low back with one hand, their faces contorted in pain that resembled either severe constipation, or going into labor, complete with rapid breathing.

We would send them for a urine sample because a kidney stone would usually irritate the patient's ureter (the tube from your kidneys to your bladder) and leave microscopic blood in the urine as a clue that the pain was due to a real kidney stone.

Tricky scheming patients, having read the *Idiot's Guide to Receiving Pain Meds in the ER,* tainted their urine samples with a few drops of blood pricked from their finger so that it objectively appeared that they were indeed experiencing a kidney stone causing microscopic blood in the urine analysis.

You learned to look for a telltale bandage on their finger...or, with the real tricksters, on their abdomen, where they had learned to prick their skin instead of their more visible finger. Pearl of wisdom for the other team: A chief complaint of kidney stone sends a huge red flag up the warning pole.

The really big red flag, complete with sparklers and dancing girls, however, was the chief complaint of back pain. Once again, it's really challenging to objectively test for back pain. Patients limped across the parking lot towards the ER entry, dramatically stopping to catch their breath; they writhed on the exam tables or asked to stand the entire time; they moaned that their backs were killing them from shoveling snow, from slipping on ice, or from picking up their infant. Sadly, their abuse forced anyone with real back pain to face a litany of skepticism whenever they showed up in the ER.

And these patients, just like Nancy, lied right to your face, no qualms whatsoever about their deceit. They lie about having never taken pain medicines before; about never visiting your clinic before; about never having had back pain before; about their allergies to non-narcotic medications; on and on.

I've had patients limp into the ER, or clinic, see me, realize we've met before in similar circumstances, and walk out waving to me with a smile, knowing it was not worth their effort, since I had just seen and busted them for lying the week before for the exact same complaint. But how to know the drug seeker if they were not on the frequent flier list?

Fortunately, there are some documented signs of narcotic-seeking behavior, starting with:

1) The aforementioned chief complaints of headache, kidney stones, or back pain, which sent warning flags wildly flapping.

2) Their regular doctor was out of town.

3) They were allergic to any pain relievers except narcotics.

4) They could not exactly remember how to pronounce the pills that had worked so well when they had last received pain medications, which was at least seventeen years ago, but sounded something like "loor-tab?" or "per-kah-set?" or "hy–hydro–hydrocodone?" As if mispronunciation, or stuttering was going to trick us into believing they had no familiarity with narcotic agents.

5) They repeatedly swore they really did not like using pills or medicines of any sort.

6) They brought their entire family, including a screaming child wearing a dirty diaper, to the visit. The noise and smell were supposed to incite a doctor to just want to get rid of them quickly, regardless of whether it involved writing out a narcotic prescription. Often, they went so far as to change the diaper while you were in the room, to help accelerate your decision to get them out of the ER.

7) When you asked what happened to cause their pain, they shared some extensive narrative, telling you about the weather in Cincinnati the day prior to their accident, family re-unions, moving furniture, and how that all related to their pain, in the most drawn-out, boring, and circuitous story that just made you want to write them a prescription for drugs and send them on their merry way rather than spending any more time in their presence than was necessary.

8) Flattery. We were repeatedly warned to watch out for patients making bold claims such as, "You're my favorite doctor. You're seriously the best doctor, you're the only one who has ever helped me, and I am so glad you're here today." Buttering up the person you're about to ask for narcotics, while enjoyable to the ears, sends up one more bright red flag.

The list continues—and there's another lengthy list of suspicious reasons for requesting prescription refills:

Their prescription of pain pills had been knocked down the drain (overused); prescription went through the laundry machine (overused); stolen from a car (overused), stolen from their purse (overused); and yes, eaten by their dog (yes, overused). I heard each of those excuses, asking for more pain pills please, multiple times in that first month.

And you cannot give in.

If you write one solitary person a prescription for narcotics, they run outside flashing the "Candy Shop is Open" sign into the clouds, like the Batman signal. A huge sign lights up over your ER, and two hours later you will have a line out the door of pain pill-seeking patients who now know that you're the new patsy on the block. And then those customers, your new best friends, will call the ER every day to find out what days you are on the schedule because they want to come say hello.

Far better to have the reputation of being a jerk known for not handing out pain pills.

But when I saw Nancy, patient number one as an ER intern, I was not yet so cynical.

In recent years, with the overdue awareness of widespread narcotic addiction, along with increasing cases of people overdosing, efforts have been made to help doctors limit the access people have to high-dose, addictive medications. But the problem still exists and it's in every community, not limited to street corners or impoverished cities, and involves every socioeconomic group. As much as I make light of an intern's daily plight of turning away patients with drug-seeking behavior, I am not making light of what I have seen narcotic addiction do to friends, to patients, to their families. It's a brutal, ugly, hard-to-help, let alone cure, disease.

LET'S MOVE ON FROM NARCOTICS; THERE WERE, AFTER ALL, OTHER patients to see and treat. One of our next ER contestants was a thirty-year-old, relatively healthy guy, who had been stung by an insect at noon. He then visited the local watering hole and drank twelve beers. Later that afternoon, through hazy-bar-lighting, bloodshot eyes, and the keen insight gained by drinking a bucket of beer, he decided he should have his swollen bug bite evaluated by medical professionals. Surprisingly, nobody at the bar offered to give up his or her barstool to drive him to the hospital.

So, our brilliantly innovative patient-to-be decided to call an ambulance to escort him to the ER because he was too drunk to drive and was feeling civically responsible. He also happened to tell the emergency operator that he was having a reaction to a bee sting.

An ambulance team rushed to pick the guy up because they were worried, rightfully from his phone call, that he was having a dangerous anaphylactic reaction to a bug bite. They whisked him to us with flashing lights and sirens.

What looked like a small mosquito bite on his arm was rapidly dismissed as not being dangerous at all, and the patient walked home.

Fortunately for the patient, Medicaid paid for that very expensive taxi ride—so the patient felt ok about it. And who paid that Medicaid bill? That's right, you and me and our taxes. Tell me we're not a socialist society, or that we don't overuse ER facilities.

To be clear, my subjective opinion is that we are able and should, as a society, provide health care to everybody. While overhauling the healthcare system will be complicated, I believe the single payor system can succeed, will be economically sound and still allows those who want, to pay to see the doctors they prefer—people just need to not abuse the system for it to function, i.e., no more free ambulance rides to evaluate mosquito bites.

Ironically, in contrast to that young, relatively healthy person feeling just fine about abusing the health system, we treated an eighty-three-year-old woman several days later, whose only medication was a multi-vitamin, and who felt terrible for taking up any of our time. She was a retired nurse who still worked sixty hours a week in her son's antique store. She was feeling embarrassed to be wasting our time with her concerns about feeling slightly tired these last months. She had refused to complain to anybody until finally that same day, someone had suggested she go to the ER because she looked ghostly pale.

It's a fine metaphor, *ghostly pale,* and her pallor truly was, somehow, completely devoid of color. Her blood hematocrit level turned out to be about 11. Hematocrit represents the red blood cell levels in your blood. Our hematocrit levels are normally in the 40s, i.e., it would have been normal for her blood to be composed of 40% red blood cells carrying oxygen, the essential food for living.

She was missing almost three-quarters of her red blood cells and kept apologizing for wasting our time. Her biggest concern was getting in trouble with her son for missing work that afternoon because we were admitting her to the ICU for an immediate blood transfusion.

She needed to go teach that thirty-year-old, bug-bit-bozo, about wasting time. Although, herein lies another good lesson: eighty-year-old women are feisty.

Case in point: several nights later another eighty-something-year-old woman was brought in by ambulance. She had been attending a Utah Jazz (basketball) game downtown and had fallen while buying a beer. Besides spilling her drink, she had also cut her forehead in the process. But she got up by herself and insisted on staying to see the end of the game.

Fortunately, a stadium usher convinced the arriving paramedic crew otherwise, because the blood spurting out of the woman's forehead was certain to land in people's drinks several rows away.

When she arrived in the ER, she was still furious with the usher for making her miss the end of a good game. The paramedics had kept pressure on her bleeding head until I stepped up heroically to take care of this spirited basketball fan.

I pulled back the gauze to see what kind of laceration I needed to fix, and—*WHOA!* Blood shot everywhere.

Merde.

She had hit an artery. I had no real idea what to do at this moment. Normally lacerations were fun to repair, and I prided myself on doing a good job—not to mention it meant I was legitimately busy and would not have to evaluate the patient vomiting in the next room. But I had no clue what to do with this lady rapidly exsanguinating in front of our eyes.

I stared down at my pager intensely, as though there was something more pressing for me to do than stop this lady from bleeding to death. I glanced up again, "Excuse me," and walked out of the room with the patient and paramedics all staring confusedly after me.

I found my attending physician and informed her of the artery hose spraying the town red from the patient's forehead.

The attending replied, "Well just close it off. Use a figure eight if you need to, OK?"

I was unsure about this plan given I had never heard of a figure eight stich, but it sounded somewhat self-explanatory. Cowboy time: sew it up, git 'r done.

I re-entered the patient's room, sat down, pulled back the gauze, and watched blood pumping up as though we had struck oil. I couldn't even see what was going on and just kept blotting at the blood, wondering if we'd need to order a blood transfusion before I was done.

The paramedics were looking at me as if to say, *Aren't you going to do something? Don't just let her slowly die after we rushed her over here for you.*

The patient glared up at me as well, likely thinking, *I could have stayed to see the game and died there slowly!*

Finally, under all this pressure to move into action, I boldly announced to everyone present, "I am going to try a figure eight stitch to stop the bleeding."

Nobody clapped.

Sewing up someone's face was usually a precise piece of work, but in this case, I just grabbed bloody tissue with forceps, trying to find anything resembling the blood vessel that was trying to hit me with its stream of fluid.

I blindly passed a large needle and thread into the flesh of the wound and put it in and out a few more times, somewhat in a figure eight, and tied it off tightly, just squeezing flesh to clamp down anything resembling tissue, and hopefully the severed blood vessels, within the suture material.

Remarkably the bleeding slowed—so I placed another similar suture and voila, the bleeding stopped. I looked up surprised at my own luck, and quickly remembered I was supposed to be confident in my actions.

After I put a long line of sutures in her temple to close the skin, she got up, sporting a very impressive black eye, and smiled at me saying, "Jeez, thought you were going to take all night, guess I missed the game."

Good lesson, sometimes you just try it.

BEHAVIORAL SCIENCE

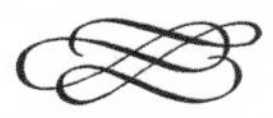

EMOTIONAL INTELLIGENCE, THE EARLY DAYS: GRUNTING

Next up on the monthly agenda for becoming a doctor: a required Behavioral Science course, several elective rotations (no call, huzzah!), and seeing clinic patients throughout. Altogether, it was scheduled to be the calmest few weeks of residency. It was to be a month without call nights or weekends working in the hospital. It was to be a month to catch up on sleep, a month to recharge for the busy winter months ahead. It was to be the most relaxing month of my entire residency, a month I was ecstatic to enjoy.

Instead, Winston arrived.

The month started with the required Behavioral Science course designed to improve our patient communication skills. The plan, which sounded simple, was to analyze videos of real encounters with our clinic patients, and then discuss ways to improve the doctor/patient relationship. Even writing about it now, it seems like a worthwhile process to improve one's doctoring skills, much like post-match analysis for professional sports teams.

First thing that needed improvement was my clinic's video system. Nobody could figure out how to run it properly. Then the machine broke. Then all the videotapes disappeared. And thus, week one was written off as a complete waste of time.

Week two seemed a mild improvement to the first week's blunders and ineptitude as we had both a working machine and tapes to record. With the video machine ready, I now needed a patient willing to have their encounter recorded.

Apparently, one area open for improvement was communicating to my patients why I needed to learn to communicate better. Asking a patient if they would mind having their medical visit filmed because I didn't know how to communicate well did very little to instill confidence with my patients (or myself for that matter).

"So, why do you want to film my visit?"

"Because we're um, you know, working to improve my communication skills with patients."

"You don't know how to talk to your patients?"

"Apparently not."

"And isn't that kind of strange, isn't this a private type of visit?"

"Yeah, you know what, you're right, forget about it."

Finally however, I filmed one single patient encounter, and we were able, on the last day of the course, to make some use of the behavioral science requirement. But first, the other resident, whose many encounters we had already been watching for two straight weeks due to her clinic having both a functioning video camera, and less discerning patients, wanted to watch herself interact on film yet again.

The fact that she had multiple visits on tape was proof enough that her communication abilities already surpassed mine, but we watched yet another heartwarming encounter of patient and physician trying and failing to ignore a camera. Which eventually led to a rousing discussion of various techniques for encouraging patients to get to the point of their visit without taking twenty minutes to tell us about several other pressing concerns that needed to be addressed beyond the one they had dallied around for the appointed visit time.

As I have pointed out, patients tended to schedule fifteen-minute appointments with one Chief Complaint and then show up with a grocery list of concerns to discuss, which rightfully required an hour's worth of time to properly explore—add that up for every patient and now you understand why doctors (ahem, me) run behind schedule. That's right, it was the patient's fault.

So far, Behavioral Science was doing a bang-up job of reaffirming my infantile defense mechanisms: *just blame the other person!*

By the way, "chief complaint" is not a term we tossed about with negative connotations, as in, *I had the biggest chief complainer in clinic today.* No, a patient's "chief complaint" is standard verbiage for the reason the person is being seen by their doctor.

Besides confirming that the patients were to blame for my consistently running behind schedule, what else did we learn in this required course? We discussed critical lessons of improving the doctor/patient relationship, like leaning over and touching a patient's knee, or grunting, to signal we were listening compassionately. Yes, the fine Art of Medicine!

Grunting was both encouraged *and* recognized as an advanced doctoring technique, signaling to your patient that you were indeed listening to their riveting complaint, and wanted them to please keep talking. And if you really aimed to score points with your advisor, you leaned forward in your video session, touched the patient's knee, *and* grunted—just, wow! You were hailed as the second coming of the family practice founding shaman.

At your next doctor visit, please compliment your family doctor if he touches your knee or grunts, these are the signs that you are in the presence of a true virtuoso.

And yes, they really did teach us these somewhat instinctual signs of non-verbal communication, because apparently what today is called Emotional Intelligence had not yet been discovered.

Remember, most medical people had been science geeks since the second grade and had experienced minimal human contact over that time. So a large part of learning to be a doctor included learning to communicate to patients. At the same time, an actual relevant problem was raised (*Wait,* you gasp, *more relevant than medical residents learning to caress their patient's knees?*); namely, the quotas and patient visit numbers that would be profitable for the large corporations that would one day employ us for mastering inefficient forms of communication.

Doctors must, according to large corporate standards, rush through their patient visits or lose their jobs. In my reality, constantly running forty-five minutes behind schedule even when I arrived in the clinic early, there was simply no time to lean over and touch everyone's knee. I might have time for a slap on the back and a "Buck up," perhaps, but the compassion thing wasted valuable time.

But still, they instructed us to grunt, squawk, and oink vocal signals, applauding our voracity if we gave encouraging "*Hmmmm*"-type thoughtful sounds to keep patients talking during encounters, demonstrating a primary caregivers' assurance to our patients that we were both listening to their enthralling story, and could not wait to hear more about their horrendous case of diarrhea.

At the same time, we were ordered to speed up all our patient visits to meet quotas. It makes for very neurotic doctors.

Final note, after watching my fellow resident's tenth videoed encounter, practicing encouraging grunts and *hmmms,* and discussing techniques at being efficient to accomplish her work, we ran out of time. We never got around to watching my tape—so don't expect any compassionate snorting from me.

At the same time that I was not learning to communicate any better, I was also seeing patients in the clinic during the afternoon, the ideal location to put into practice what I was learning about efficiency and time management.

My schedule was usually running behind by the time the patient ever got around to discussing why they had actually come to see me. There existed some unspoken game, one I never asked to play, whereby clinic patients, on a quest to keep my schedule running late, often hid the reason for their doctor visit behind a trickle of trifling discomforts, such as a mild rash that did not currently happen to be present, and then, at the last possible second, when our scheduled time was ended, they pounced on you with a complaint you could not ignore.

I could regularly expect to write out my medical instructions for treating a patient's intermittent hand-numbness, headaches, and overactive bladder; have handed over their prescriptions, doffed my hat, said my farewells, and be walking out the exam room door—when suddenly the patient triumphantly exclaimed, "Ha! Ha! Surprise! The hand numbness was a ruse, I'm really here because my rectum itches!" Or more likely, that was when they mentioned the chest pain and shortness of breath with exertion that demanded I stay and further evaluate a potential heart condition.

As an intern I felt it my medical and moral duty to sit back down and delve into the fascinating tales of *pruritic ani (itchy rectum)* while the rest of my patients sat impatiently awaiting my arrival. That was our job, taking care of the patient's problems.

By the time I was a third-year resident, my answer to such last-minute requests was a terse, "Go ahead and make an appointment at the front desk on your way out, and we can discuss it next week." *One visit, one problem.*

But early in training, you felt it was your job to help everyone with everything. Which made me late and tense, which made the rest of the patients unhappy, which made my clinic manager upset, and triggered her to start barking at me repeatedly that I was forty minutes behind schedule, which left me more tense, and the patients glommed onto that energy and requested more time—and you can see why my degree of stress climbed to unhealthy levels.

In my clinic, it did not take too many months to become convinced that patients existed with the sole purpose of wasting time.

As a patient, when I call to make a doctor's appointment, I have a specific reason for visiting. It starts with, "Hi, I need to see a doctor."

"Very good, and why do you want to see the doctor?"

"Because I poked my eye out."

And as a physician, when my appointments were booked closely together, I introduced myself to my patients saying something like, "Hi, my name is John, I'm the doctor here today. What brings you in?" Right to the point, let's get to your reason for being here today.

At this point a patient's logical reply to my question should be something like, "I'm here because I can't see out of my eye. I poked it with a fondue skewer." However, for some half-baked reason not known to man or woman, most patient responses had more to do with the potato salad Aunt Marcy cooked up last week, and their concern about recurrent belching ever since, than the real concern regarding the eye being poked out.

At the same time, the supposed reason why they made the appointment was typed on my patient schedule list. But without fail, the person with "skin rash" written down as the reason for their visit not only wanted to discuss the rash on their toes, but also how to stop smoking, the possibility of receiving a pap smear that day, that they, "Just didn't feel right," *and*, "Oh yes, just remembered, my husband said to tell you I've experienced chest pain with exertion during the last month, I think it's anxiety, but my dad died of a heart attack at my age, but I think if you just write me for some Xanax I'll be fine. Ok?"

I am being slightly flippant—but not very, that list of complaints is pretty accurate for what patients expected taken care of during our scheduled fifteen-minute clinic appointment.

And when I mentioned, "That's a lot to get through in our

scheduled fifteen minutes--" their reply would be, "That's ok, let's just leave the chest pain for another day, that was my spouse being worried."

Why in the name of all things sane, rational, warm, and fluffy, did they not ever lead with the bit about the chest pain?

I don't know. Total medical mystery that left me wondering if the clinic was filming my patient encounters whilst sending in comedic actors as pretend patients to teach me better patient skills. And my ensuing frustration was to be mollified when I eventually learned to practice the art of medicine.

Instead of crying, leaving the profession or yelling at the patient, I was to follow the art of medicine recommendations about smiling compassionately, touching the patient's leg or shoulder, and making those agreeable barnyard grunts, to let them know I was listening and wanted them to continue with their riveting tale of chest discomfort.

At which point we got to the heart of the matter: "But write me the prescription for Xanax just in case." Yes, sneaking in the innocent request for controlled substances pervaded every aspect of medicine.

What was our answer to such requests? The art of medicine instructed us to go ahead and dole out handfuls of anti-depressants like Halloween candy because, according to primary care studies, depression was vastly under-diagnosed and under-treated. But not on Family Practice Watch! Again, they really did teach this stuff.

The point being, the art of primary care involved covering as many topics as possible that were relevant to your patient's health —and never forgetting that depression, anxiety, and other mental health issues, were vastly under-diagnosed, so start almost every patient on anti-depressants.

While the art of medicine taught you how to interact with your patients, staff, and fellow physicians, it was the patients in the equation who messed up everything. As stated, it was surprisingly difficult to even ascertain the simple reason why most patients were in the clinic to begin with. Imagine the confusion when we headed into complex issues, like whether or not they had experienced a fever with their illness. I'm getting an itchy rash myself just thinking of asking about fevers.

A patient might tell me, "I have a cough that won't go away."

Well, that's straightforward, and I might follow up with a return question in this opening rally: "Have you had a fever with the cough?"

While most patients appeared to have the physical ability to nod yes or no, they instead chose to launch into a diatribe on their temperature: "Well, last week I felt warm, but that might have been the enchiladas I had at lunch. I usually don't eat Mexican, but Aunt Gertie made a mole. Do you eat mole? I love mole. Am I boring you? Ok, because ever since that mole, I think my temperature has run warm, for me, I mean."

Based upon patients I saw during my residency years, most adults in the United States, people with the right to vote for elected officials, associate their health issues with food that was prepared by their aunts the previous week. Yet these same people, making complex gastronomic associations, apparently had psychological avoidance issues related to answering *yes or no* questions.

These same people were also *incredibly* in tune with their body's thermoregulation—which was surprising, because the average 320-pound individual who smoked, did not exercise, and had not seen their toes in decades, somehow knew their body's precise idling temperature for different hours of the day.

I would listen to the same person who scoffed at my suggestion that inhaling dangerous volumes of fast-food combined with a complete lack of exercise since conception, was contributing to their weight gain, uncontrolled diabetes and back pain—that same person, ignoring everything I said, would become fervently concerned that their temperature was 98.9 on the clinic thermometer because, "I always run 98.7. That's a fever for me. Do you think I need antibiotics? I think I need antibiotics. Write me for antibiotics. Zithromax works. Actually, make it a double, my neighbor gets it too." (a verbatim statement from a patient).

I think you need to get off the couch, is what I wanted to say, but instead, the *art of medicine* dictated that I touch their knee and grunt my approval at their insight.

Regardless, I still had no idea why they were there.

So no, despite lectures on communication, it appeared I had a lot left to learn.

INTERMISSION I: WINSTON ARRIVES

Despite not learning a tremendous amount, I did enjoy these first days of no call, sleeping in my own house every night, and arriving at the clinic during normal work hours. It was lovely to rest and recover, and to look forward to a few days' vacation over the holidays.

However, I really do not recall much of those weeks so preciously allotted for my recuperation because the girl I had started dating decided to give me a dog.

I grew up with dogs. I love dogs. I looked forward to having lots of time to spend with a dog one day, later, when I had a life. (Apparently that time has now arrived as my wife and I currently have four dogs, and foster litters of rescued puppies because my kids say so. But that is *now.* Back then, I did not have time for a puppy.)

The culpable dog-gifting woman, who I had dated for several months, was a brilliant, tough-as-nails, hardworking surgical resident, who was therefore all too aware of how little time an intern, or surgical resident, could dedicate to caring for a puppy. Busy schedules with call nights away from home, and weekends in the hospital, did not make for a puppy-friendly life—not to mention puppies are expensive and I was already living check to check due to some previous financial blunders prior to, and including, medical school, the undoubted fiscal gaffe highlight in a life of financial blunders.

When the woman I was dating had earlier suggested getting a puppy, I had said, "No." I said, "No puppy." And I freely admit I am not good at saying "No," but I said it, many times. My voice did not waver, and nothing in my tone waffled, or suggested, "No, but I'm open to discussion."

But one fine December evening as I lay sleeping, catching up on months of sleep deprivation, dreaming of that relaxing week of vacation waiting for me, an eight-week-old yellow lab puppy was dropped on my bed.

Who can resist an eight-week-old yellow lab puppy? Not me. My supposedly relaxing days ahead evaporated and the month became the single most stressful and sleepless time of my entire residency.

Any discussion of Winston would best be put under a discussion of pediatrics. Granted, there was no nine-month waiting period to prepare for his sudden arrival, but that is what a puppy is, really—a little guy that cannot take care of himself, who rapidly matures into acting like a two-year-old kid for most of its adult life.

Adding to my stress was the fact that I was renting a friend's basement, and she did not want a dog in her house, let alone a puppy whose raison d'etre was to chew, poop, and pee in an effort to destroy any household willing to take him in for the day.

It also happened to be the first December in a long time that our city received snow for the entire month. The nights I had warmly anticipated going to bed early and catching up on missed sleep were instead spent taking Winston outside to go to the bathroom in a snowstorm all night long. Every night I should have been sleeping, I instead stood in my underwear, peeing along with Winston under snowing skies, cursing the girlfriend.

Days were a crazed mix of dropping him at friend's houses, leaving him in the kitchen for a few hours, running home from the hospital to find urine and poop spread everywhere, and any objects within reach, destroyed.

This was not a Christmas gift; this was chaos on an occasional leash.

Winston came to dominate my life, a tiny bit like those boys and girls that keep all you parents awake and stressed and scared. (a statement I can now amend having had three kids since then—puppies are stressful, but kids are in a different stratosphere altogether.) And he didn't get much better with age. Many people over the next years told me that Winston reminded them of the dog in the book *Marley and Me* (a book I did not read knowing there would be a final chapter)—except worse, much worse.

As my sleep became non-existent and I scrambled to find places for him to stay during the daytime, I thought more seriously about sending him back, certain that he would find a good home. All my friends kept telling me to send him back—even the girlfriend now admitted it was probably best to take him back.

Then one night I took Winston cross-country skiing (he didn't ski, I tucked him into a backpack on my chest with his head sticking out to take in the view). I got out of the car in a dark canyon parking lot and was jarringly scared witless by two enormous dogs, a hippopotamus- sized Rottweiler mix and a huge German shepherd, who both bounded from the woods, viciously barking and baring fangs at me.

But before I even had time to gasp with fear, a ten-week-old blur of yellow launched himself out of the car. Winston planted himself between me and those two enormous growling beasts. He barked right back at them, baring his puppy teeth with equal ferocity, standing his ground while both I, and the two large dogs, stood stunned and speechless.

No way I could send back this guy who was fearlessly standing up to certain death to protect me. It was almost a scary feeling to have that kind of unconditional love and protection around you. An adored and devoted little guy who would try my patience on a regular basis, to an ungodly degree, for many years ahead.

Tales of Winston show up in the future, but for now, along with everything else I might mention in the hospital, know that Winston and his surrounding state of disaster were what waited for me outside the hospital stress and exhaustion.

INPATIENT PEDIATRICS —VEASEY TEAM

HOOFS AND HEARTS NOBODY CAN HEAR (AT LEAST NOT ME)

The Family Practice program required that we spend several months working on the in-patient pediatric teams at the children's hospital. The teams in this case were the *Veasey* team, which cared for all the hospital's cardiac patients; and the *Lahey* team, caring for and treating all the young oncology patients. The patients without heart or cancer problems were picked to join respective teams by our captains. I had long since abandoned any hopes that "teams" meant we would play games together.

But all was not lost. The children's hospital, despite being overrun with the munchkin cast from *The Wizard of Oz,* was an amazing place with snack carts on every corner, games for kids to play, movies to watch, and bald ten-year-old patients receiving chemotherapy running through the halls pushing their IV poles.

For this pediatric rotation I joined the *Veasey* team, where I anticipated being intimidated by pediatric cardiologists and the wee, tiny, beating hearts under their care.

To begin with, I barely understood cardiology. In adult cardiology we concerned ourselves with trying to listen to grown-up hearts beating at audible rates. When you think of a beating heart, you might think of the pulse in your wrist, or the pounding in your chest, i.e. a single beat from the pumping heart. If you listen with a stethoscope however, you will typically hear *two* heart sounds, *"Lub-Dub."* Those two sounds are made by the closing of heart valves: The *Lub* sound is made by the mitral and tricuspid valves closing on the right side of your heart; and the *Dub* sound comes from the Aortic and Pulmonary valves closing on the left side. Good so far? The heart valves prevent blood from flowing backwards into the wrong chamber of the heart—the blood should move forward in your body when the heart muscles squeeze together, not in reverse; it's not efficient.

In typical adults, the heart beats 60 to 80 times a minute, and we would listen carefully for any abnormalities to the healthy "Lub-Dub." What types of abnormalities? A heart murmur was usually pretty obvious to hear: instead of hearing the normal and healthy, *"Lub-Dub, Lub-Dub"* of two heart valves closing (which is starting to sound like an old sea-shanty), you heard: "Lub-shhhhh-Dub" as blood squirted out between an errant valve that was not able to shut properly. And then we rated the murmur by how loud it sounded with scores from 1-6. A score of "one" was quiet enough to be missed, while a "six" from the Albanian judge meant you could hear it without using a stethoscope, i.e. you better not miss it.

Murmurs might occur in an otherwise healthy person when excess blood was flowing through a body (such as with pregnancy), or if a person had a fever and their heart was beating especially fast. But our concern was with murmurs triggered by damaged valves—perhaps scarred over and chewed up by bacteria during a previous case of rheumatic heart disease. Such damage allowed blood to flow backwards through the valve when it should not (called regurgitation), or perhaps it was so scarred that it could not fully open and therefore limited outward blood flow (stenosis)—either way creating poor cardiac output. If the valves were so diseased that the blood flow became highly inefficient, it was possible for a person to go into heart failure, eventually requiring surgery to replace the damaged valve with a brand-new mechanical or pig valve.

There were also extra sounds to listen for, sounds that shouldn't be present in a healthy heart, called S3 or S4 "gallops." Sick adults lay in bed while I closed my eyes and listened to their hopefully beating heart with my stethoscope. I kept tempo with my fingers, tapping on their chest, trying to decipher if the rhythm sounded like the normal "Lub-Dub, Lub-Dub;" or more like, "TENN-a-seee, Tenn-a-seee;" or perhaps, "ken-TUH-key, ken-Tuh-key."

I then needed to remember which of these extra heart sounds, S3 or S4, sounded like "ken-TUH-kee" and which one was "TENN-a-see." Only to be told by the attending cardiologist that I was a Lub-Dub who was hearing things, and that the patient had a normal heart exam.

The chastisement was expected due to its consistency. I shrugged it off, more interested in knowing if doctors in other countries also used the names of U.S. heartland states to describe galloping heart sounds, or were cardiologists nationalistic? Were Italian residents tapping patients' chests, debating if they were hearing "mi-LAN-oh, mi-LAN-oh," instead of, "NAH-po-lee, NAH-po-lee?"

Would I eventually get into a knockdown, barroom brawl at some international resident conference vehemently debating whether a heartbeat sounded more like "duh-BROV-nik—duh-BROV-nik," or simple horse-country states—which we can all agree are at least related to the word *"gallop"* in the first place. I'm relatively certain Dubrovnik has little to do with horses and galloping and therefore was a ridiculous word to use to describe the sound of the heart at all.

And the poor Mexican resident might as well have had his ears painted on. "Gua-da-la-HAH-RAH?" Are you kidding me? Not to mention, I have little fear of getting beaten up by arrogant international medical residents, not because I'm tough at all, I will just never, ever, attend an international resident conference.

I am also now keenly aware of why the Argentine cardiology fellow, the one who never taught me how to do a proper history and physical exam in medical school (*Playing Doctor; Part One*), was so confused; no heartbeat sounds like, "Bue-nos AI-RES."

OK, international cardiac equestrian tangents aside, let's get back to evaluating pediatric hearts, which makes diagnosing adult heart problems seem like child's play (a confusing metaphor when discussing kids in the first place). Yes, figuring out the infant-sized pumping machine sounds we were now supposed to interpret was one of the bigger challenges I'd yet faced in residency. Was I up to the task?

No.

We were somehow presumed to ascertain the variety of things that could go wrong with pediatric hearts—such as blood vessels being attached in the wrong order, walls not closing between heart chambers, blood vessels being too narrow, etc. And we did this all based on careful diagnostic skills, such as listening to the child's heart, measuring blood pressures, and feeling his or her pulses.

Try listening to an infant's heart. It's a joke. Seriously. You might as well listen to, and attempt to count, the sound of a hummingbird's wing flapping, or dance to the wheezing whine of a leprechaun's bagpipes—either one was more realistic to hear than me listening to a newborn's heart and imagining I could interpret the sounds.

Have you ever felt a newborn babe's beating chest? Their heart pounds away at close to the speed of light. How are you supposed to hear, let alone differentiate *anything*, when you are listening to something that sounds like the little drummer boy on crack cocaine after three shots of espresso? You can't hear a goddamn thing in between those 3,000 beats a second.

And let's not forget, kids don't lie still like sick and fatigued adults. They don't stop gurgling or making baby noises; instead, once a cold stethoscope touches their warm skin, they start screeching. And believe me, I wasn't dipping my stethoscope in ice water before I touched them, but you'd think I had impaled their chest with one of my many drug-rep donated pens. You'd think they didn't care about my trying to help them one bit.

Yet, despite my inability to properly identify heart sounds under ideal conditions and place them in their respective-sounding equine states, the pediatric cardiology attending insisted we should hear some random murmur in-between the fluttering newborn heartbeats, and over the kid's belching and crying—a heartwarming encounter that usually ended with me being spit up on or sprayed with urine. And in case you're concerned for the infant, we were of course instructed to warm the stethoscope in our hands before triggering their inevitable squawking fuss.

Regardless of my faulty listening skills, it was quite amazing to think these kid's lives were being saved. Certainly not thanks to me. Those cardiologists rarely slept and wow, they had great hearing. Maybe great ears were a requirement for becoming a pediatric cardiologist? If they planned on grading me based on my hearing skills alone, I might as well have walked home that first day.

Beyond the not so simple act of attempting to care for the patients, we also had to contend with being in the children's hospital in February. Children's hospitals are busy places any time of year, but during the winter months they become varying zones of bedlam with a steady supply of junk food.

The dreaded rumors about the sheer volume of work being punctuated by a non-stop barrage of pager alerts were unfortunately accurate. While you called to answer one page, the blasted thing rang three more times. I drained the batteries in my pager four times that month. But at some point, as you staggered to the ER for the twentieth time in one night to admit yet one more sick little patient, meandering past bleary-eyed kids rolling their IV stands to the hallway's play-station, and along the way received two more pages telling you that you had two more patients waiting to be admitted, and another four pages from nurses needing you right away to evaluate sick patients on three different floors, a calmness overtook you.

I would smile, and start whistling, because there was no physical, earthly way I could be in five places at once, and eventually, there was a blissfulness in knowing that at some point the next day, I would get to go home for a few hours (to clean up dog poop and pee)—and one day, far, far away, I would no longer be in residency.

And despite the chaos, I liked the children's hospital for two reasons besides the funny little patients. First, they provided good scrubs: green and comfortable; Second, the food was on the decent side for hospital standards. There are annual magazine ratings for hospitals around the country, and there are rating guides for restaurants—I think somebody should do a combined rating guide for hospital cuisine. Hospital food rankings might be a justifiable reason for choosing one hospital over another. These were bastions of health care, for the Hippocratic oath's sake, and the food was taking years off everyone's life.

They had placed a Burger King in our University hospital. Fast food contributes to obesity, hypertension, increases your risk of a heart attack and diabetes, which contributes to sexual dysfunction (thereby increasing everyone's tension), and probably lowers your immune system—overall it was killing our country, making people ill and unable to fight off infection and therefore, the perfect match for any hospital group wishing to stay in business and make profits. The only person making bigger profits was probably the Starbucks barista.

Caffeine in a hospital?

Priceless.

The coffee cart was a goldmine, likely raking in more cash than any of the doctors. We dreamed of such luxuries back in the other hospitals where we were told to enjoy the dirty water called coffee (Starbucks built a lovely coffee shop there after I left).

One of the problems with going to different hospitals, beyond being made jealous by better scrubs and decent coffee we would never experience at our community barracks, was the nitty-gritty stuff—like acquiring necessary parking passes and meal cards. These logistics might sound like trite issues, but try being late for your first day of work, unable to get into the parking garage at 5:30 in the morning when it's 12 degrees outside (Fahrenheit), because the security people in charge of passes were only in the office from 9:32 until 10:35 on odd-numbered days, and required not only your car's registration, but also a note from your mother, the top from a cereal box of Lucky Charms, and a secret handshake before they would consider giving you a parking pass. Receiving a parking pass, however, was a walk in the park compared to the begging and groveling that was required to receive food cards.

When your twenty-four-hour day consists of no sleep, quantifying bodily fluids, listening to people's complaints, and feeling intellectually inadequate—you really looked forward to certain things, like eating. Unfortunately, before laying my grubby paws on the food cards I needed to pay for meals in the children's hospital cafeteria, I discovered I needed a dictation code.

What does a dictation code have to do with my ability to eat? The code was needed so that I could dictate all the patient charts left by the family practice resident that had preceded me in the hospital and returned to Wyoming leaving a pile of thirty charts that for some reason had become my responsibility to dictate, or I would not get those food cards.

Our program invited family practice residents from neighboring states lacking a designated children's hospital, to work here due to the amazing teaching offered. And I now officially make a motion to revoke all those invitations because those residents never finished their chart work. And until the charts were finished, the hospitals could not bill the patients and therefore could not be paid. So, residency administration people decided that the residents responsible for the hospital not being paid were family practice residents, and therefore, family practice residents were to be responsible for their brethren's laziness and could not eat until the hospital was paid. That's a long way of saying I was left without food cards. That's right, until I completed the abandoned charts, I would not be given the cards that paid for my food.

I then sat through a bureaucratic nightmare whereby I was forced to find spare time to dictate charts on patients I had never seen, otherwise I would never eat because my credit cards were tapped out, and I barely had enough cash saved to cover rent. Until every single delinquent chart was understood and dictated, the hold on my food would not be removed. And when the super-friendly woman who retrieved the charts from the medical records room could not find one for me to dictate—somehow that also meant that I could not get my food cards because I had not dictated the chart on the patient I had never seen, and whose chart was missing due to no fault of mine what-so-bloody ever.

I seem to have some pent-up frustration regarding those charts.

And lastly, you needed a security pass that would allow you access to the patient hallways. On the last night of your service, the code expired promptly at 12 a.m. Remarkably, at 12 a.m. on the last day of the month, I also happened to be on call.

It was actually not remarkable at all because being the intern from "family practice" meant that you were normally given the worst call schedule, which meant being on-call on the last day of each month so that you finished one rotation at 7 a.m., and then ran to start a new rotation at a different hospital where you were required to have arrived at 6 a.m.—which was not physically feasible without crossing a time zone.

And there I was on-call at 12 a.m. on my last night, and at that moment a code was called. I happened to be in between hallway doors when my passcode stopped working. As the code went off, I was stuck between two security doors, unable to go anywhere for twenty minutes until somebody happened to open the door for me. It seemed to be symbolic of my residency experience.

And you might ask, "Why not get all those administrative issues taken care of the month before that new rotation starts?" Because you were working every second until then and usually on call until 7 a.m. the morning of which you are due to start the rotation in a different hospital.

My days on the actual pediatric rotation were spent in a confused haze of admitting sick kids, discharging slightly healthier kids, and attempting to decipher the different heart rhythms that all sound identical when the heart beats like a high-pitched jack hammer.

As mentioned, on pediatric rotations in the winter, I had a complete lack of sleep on call nights, followed by floating through a post-call fog the following day.

I'm not sure if it was merely due to sleep deprivation, or perhaps breathing hospital air, or perhaps it was the children's hospital happy-smiling bright décor, but all of it added up to a hallucinatory sensation that fooled you into believing you were almost merry. Perhaps it was similar to a condition called "ICU-psychoses," whereby patients drugged in the ICU, sedated, intubated, and anesthetized while being poked, stuck, and prodded throughout their bodies for weeks on end, developed a strange mental state to survive. This psychosis, a sort of hazy mental state that did not accept their reality, was believed to be what the patients required to survive the otherwise hellacious ICU experience. Perhaps the post-call pseudo-merriment was a similar defense mechanism, not too far removed from that of ICU patients, that helped you survive those long weeks.

Being post-call is nice because it means you will eventually get to go home that day. But the post-call haze after a sleepless night also led me into some interesting situations.

One morning, post-call, I stumbled out of the morning report room needing to go to the bathroom. Feeling quite stylish in my green scrubs and long white coat with ring around the collar, I strode into the restroom and sat down in a bathroom stall. Someone wearing cowboy boots sat down in the adjoining stall, and a minute later started singing. There was something slightly amiss. It was not so much the singing in a bathroom stall part that bothered me; the problem was that the soprano voice seemed out of place in the men's room, as did the singer's pink boots.

I peered out through the stall and watched somebody who had just entered walk to the sink, where to my horror I realized they were doing a makeup check. My mind recounted the steps into the bathroom, and I mentally checked off the lack of urinals. I was trapped in the women's bathroom. In France, there were co-ed bathrooms, but not in the USA where I was now going to be arrested, or at least kicked out of residency for being a pervert trying to watch women go to the bathroom—this was awful, no recovering now. Do I just walk out? Damn post-call psychoses!

Along with treating cardiac patients and being politely told I was clueless regarding the pediatric heart, we spent most of the month admitting little guys and girls with the dreaded respiratory syncytial virus, RSV. (Similarly dangerous to RUVs, for you *Princess Bride* fans, and fully described in Playing Doctor, *Part One: Medical School*). Just like in medical school, it was not uncommon to discharge thirty patients from our team on a given day, and to admit another thirty-six—just a nightmare of paperwork for interns.

Lastly, we had a bunch of frequent fliers—usually patients with infected shunts (a tube from their brain that allows extra fluid to drain off into their body), or chemotherapy patients with fevers who returned frequently due to their illnesses.

Since the chemotherapy patients went to the *Lahey* team, my team took over care of all the kids with infected shunts. Ashton was one such frequent flyer whose shunt to his brain became infected on a very regular basis. He was a precocious little four-year-old that everyone enjoyed seeing—except for whichever resident had to deal with him at 4 a.m. every night, as he stayed up watching reruns of *Barney* at decibel volumes on par with AC/DC concerts.

Ashton's mother also had a reputation for several interesting reasons. First, she had been caught propositioning doctors in the elevator, and parents in the hallways for sexual favors on a regular basis. Secondly, she had on repeated occasions worn pilfered scrubs and walked around the hospital acting like a nurse, taking unwitting physician's orders, and trying to administer medicine. They made her sign a contract not to do these things anymore. Is a contract with somebody who does these things in the first place legally binding? My guess? Not likely.

And while it was never proven, there was a concern for something called Munchausen Syndrome by Proxy, whereby parents or caregivers make up illnesses or cause children under their care to become sick. Given the frequency with which Ashton was admitted to the hospital, and how much his mother seemed to enjoy her time there as well, we discussed the possibility of her being guilty of this syndrome but could never find evidence.

Mostly, what I learned on pediatrics, apart from the impossible fantasy of listening to newborn heart beats, is that pediatric medicine involves learning to take care of parents with comfort and assurance, because the kids usually recovered. Unlike many adult patients, kids wanted to get better. Kids didn't pretend to be in pain in the hospital, they didn't want to be there, and they bounced back quickly. Damn those little heartbreakers.

MEANWHILE WINSTON, THE LABRADOR PUPPY WITH BIG SAD heartbreaking eyes, destroyed everything within his reach to make sure all was not quiet on the home front. Most mornings I tried finding friends willing to keep him at their house during the day, but those bridges were rapidly burned in the wake of his demolition skills. Occasionally I just left him in the kitchen with food and water, returning to find urine and poop spread amongst heaps of random shredded household items I could not fathom how he had retrieved. This was my downtime, and it was becoming more stressful than my life as an intern.

RURAL MEDICINE, COALVILLE

ONE TINY SHOULDER, ONE MASSIVE PROBLEM

In an effort to influence a percentage of future physicians to work in small, out-of-the-way towns where doctors were needed, the residency program demanded we spend one month working in a rural setting. It was kind of a marketing ploy, maybe semantics, but "rural medicine" sounds a lot more appealing than being packed off to practice "backwoods medicine." Much like chefs changing the name of the Toothfish to Chilean Sea Bass, it was supposed to sound more appealing—although I don't think rural medicine sales went through the roof quite the same way as the fish. Either way, I could only be so rural, given Winston the wonder pup was now part of my life, and I could not leave him and travel to some faraway Montana setting complete with feuding clans and rivers running through it.

Instead, I found myself working for Norman Rockwell's physician poster child, the epitome of a small-town doctor, in a rustic town called Coalville, only an hour's drive from Salt Lake City. If you don't know where to find Coalville, it's on the way to Evanston.

This doctor had delivered generations of all the surrounding farm's babies; he owned and staffed clinics in two neighboring towns; treated people in the local prison and nursing homes; scrubbed in to assist on his patient's surgeries; and drove to the "big city" to see his patients when they were in hospital. He had been on-call, twenty-four hours a day, seven days a week, 365 days a year for the last 187 years. People *adored* him. Every single patient that visited the clinic pulled me aside to tell me what a great doctor he was, how much they loved him, and how lucky I was to work alongside this icon. The atmosphere might have been nauseating—except, he genuinely was a great guy.

Somewhat ironically, it was here, in a rural setting, that I was first introduced to writing patient notes on a computer. Crazy, I know, but modern medicine in the year 2000 did not yet include all hospitals using electronic health records. I sat in the exam room with patients and took notes directly onto the computer. I quickly discovered it was very hard to do those eye- contact, knee-touching, grunt-approving personal touches I had been trained to perform while hunting for the letter "*Q*" on the keyboard.

Rural medicine, apart from surprising me with its more technologically advanced record keeping, was exactly what I had imagined: taking care of everyone and everything that walks in the door—it was just medicine, cowboy medicine, in fact. The doctor, literally a cowboy hat- and boot-wearing man, performed all sorts of medical procedures and treatments because there was nobody else out there in the wild west to do them.

Ok, it was not quite the wild frontier. We were not very far away from some big hospitals; but his patients preferred to see him instead of trusting any new age, fancy young doctors—and doesn't it sound more exciting to imagine we were performing surgeries after sterilizing our steak knives over a campfire? And there really was a cowboy's flair to what he was willing to treat, and therefore, somehow expected me to be willing to treat as well.

I had barely been versed in certain procedures, such as injecting people's joints with medication. So, I hesitated (responsibly, I thought) the first time this doctor told me, "Why don't you go into room four and inject Mr. Thomas' right knee with Kenalog."

I replied, "Well, I've never actually injected anybody's knee with Kenalog before." Rationally thinking it best to receive some instruction before plunging a large needle full of steroids into Mr. Thomas.

The doctor looked me up and down with a combination of disappointment and disgust, stating, "Well just get in there and do it, then. How else you gonna learn?"

I couldn't argue with that logic and started walking reluctantly towards the room containing poor Mr. Thomas and his soon to be doomed knee. I glanced mournfully back over my shoulder, "I really don't know what I'm do--"

"Ok, fine. I'll show you this time, but you do it from now on, OK?" And he gave me a quick tutorial into injecting a knee. I performed all the joint injections after that.

I will now admit, with a little bit of chagrin, that the cowboy medicine attitude served me well. There were many, many times in the future when I would walk into a patient's room about to perform a procedure, and the patient would ask something like, "Have you done this before?"

And I would laugh, saying something like: "Nah, but I just watched it on YouTube, looks pretty simple."

And the patient would chuckle and relax, having no idea that my calm reply, which he took for confident humor, was completely accurate. No bad outcomes though.

I did learn quite a lot from this doctor besides where to find the letter Q on a keyboard, and how to inject steroids into Mr. Thomas. We did everything from treating chopped-off fingers, to removing lipomas, to diagnosing and treating Alzheimer's disease. I looked on with amazement as he told patients they had

Alzheimer's. I thought you needed a neurologist in a fancy hospital with expensive books and laboratory tests to tell somebody they had Alzheimer's disease.

Nope.

If somebody over the age of fifty strolled into the clinic and happened to mention being forgetful, they were diagnosed with Alzheimer's disease, and started on medication.

I was occasionally forgetful, but I thought it was partly selective, and mostly due to sleep deprivation; but maybe I had early onset Alzheimer's? No way I was mentioning that tasty tidbit to Dr. Roy Rogers, or I would be roped and force-fed a handful of psychiatry medications that might leave me goofy and wanting to learn how to lasso.

Besides prescribing mind-altering pharmaceuticals, he also liked playing with his flex-sigmoid scope to screen patients for colon cancer. He even let me steer a camera up somebody's intestine. He was crazy, this rectal-colon stuff was for specialists who liked being up inside a patient's ass, not for we simple Family Practice folk who liked to sing and dance around the caring physician campfire. But good rural doctors learn everything they can to provide their towns with comprehensive, up-to-date, proper medical care—and this guy was as good as any doctor I ever met.

A typical day: As the sun rose in the East, our rural medicine adventure began with covering a variety of locations requiring medical attention. We started in the local hospital, scrubbing into the OR to assist a general surgeon in removing a patient's gallbladder. Recall from my surgery rotation that I had spent a month assisting on the removal of pesky gallbladders, so I looked like a total pro answering all the typical gallbladder questions. Which might have set me up to look like I knew what I was doing—at least it filled me with some confidence that morning.

Then off to prison to prescribe ibuprofen for twisted ankles—which I also confidently examined and diagnosed (ibuprofen was a hotly traded commodity in prison, and therefore quite valuable).

Next, a visit to the nursing home—very sad to see people lying there, not quite alert, or responsive, who I imagined at one point had some interesting stories to tell us about their lives. While we were evaluating the newly arrived nursing home patients, we received a call that a patient was in labor at the hospital and very close to delivery.

We rushed back to the hospital and met a young Spanish-speaking woman lying in bed about to deliver a baby. I knew nothing about this pregnant woman, but I was prepared for a nice straightforward delivery. I believe the boy scouts motto was *be prepared*—it was better to be prepared for everything, and not have anything happen, than the other way around.

I had lasted two weeks in the boy scouts.

We entered the makeshift delivery room and met the patient's nurse, who quickly informed us, "Oh good, you made it, I have no training in this stuff."

No problem, I did. I had lots of OB training; not to mention I was brimming with confidence from my morning of appearing experienced in simple patient cases.

I introduced myself to the woman in labor, put on gloves, and started coaching her through her contractions. I felt confident telling her when to push, when to relax. My obstetrics training flooded back to me no problem, and everything was going along beautifully as I started to help bring her baby into the world—even my Spanish was flowing nicely.

I controlled the delivery of the baby's head perfectly, preventing any vaginal lacerations that would have needed to be repaired (I prided myself on performing very controlled deliveries so I could tell my women friends that my patients rarely had vaginal tears. There's something to chisel onto my tombstone).

But before I had time to congratulate myself on a stellar delivery of the kid's head, the baby stopped coming out.

He just stopped.

I looked down, waiting for the rest of the baby to appear—but nothing happened. The head was out, the neck was being tightly squeezed, but the shoulder, usually the next body part to appear, was nowhere to be seen.

I added some gentle traction to help deliver the shoulder—but nothing moved, the head remained the only visible part of the baby.

I heard the relaxed voice of the doctor behind me whispering, *"Okay, deliver the shoulder."*

Very calmly I replied, "Yup. I am. I'm trying to deliver the shoulder." (All my time in cowboy country had me saying things like, "yup" instead of "yes." I guess we're all lucky I didn't shout *Giddy'up pardner, let's get r' done!*)

"Well, let's get it out then."

"Uh-huh, that's what I'm doing, delivering the shoulder--"

But the shoulder had no intention of being delivered.

The problem we were encountering is called shoulder dystocia, and the subtle encouragements being whispered in my ear were not the slightest bit helpful.

Shoulder dystocia occurs when the baby's shoulder gets stuck behind the mother's pubic symphysis (pelvic bone); thereby not allowing the baby to descend any further out of the mother.

The baby was unable to move out into the world, and you can't exactly shove the kid's head back inside. Shoulder dystocia is one of the more anxiety-provoking complications you can unexpectedly face in an otherwise normal delivery.

Why? Well, in that compressed position, there's not a lot of oxygen making it to the infant's brain, so, permanent brain damage is one concern; death is another. Thus, high anxiety for everyone involved wanting to get the kid out quickly.

With the kid stuck in this dangerously compressed position, I started mentally racing through the shoulder dystocia chapter of my obstetrics book. I remembered this much: shoulder dystocia was potentially a very bad situation for everyone in the room.

I mentally flipped the page to the variety of maneuvers you could attempt to dislodge the baby. The maneuvers to get beyond this dangerous entrapment ranged from conservative efforts, like applying supra-pubic pressure to release the trapped shoulder, or rotating the baby inside the mother, hoping to dislodge the shoulder; all the way to more violent actions, such as breaking the baby's clavicle (ouch), cutting the mother's pubic symphysis in half (Double-ouch), or returning to the O.R. for an emergency caesarian section.

I attempted to appear calm while frantically running my brain over those proper obstetric protocols. But rather than any appropriate initial maneuver coming to mind, my brain was shouting, *"Break the clavicle! Break the clavicle! Cut the pubic symphysis! Cut it now!"*

Fortunately, I resisted the temptation to make a reactionary ass of myself—first things first, get the patient's legs back and try applying fundal pressure (pressing down on the mother's uterus), and pressure to the pelvic bone to try and dislodge the shoulder.

Nothing.

Time to try rotating the baby internally. I put my hands inside the mother, grasping the wet, slimy fellow, best I could, and twisted him gently—then more forcefully—and then, even more forcefully, to the point I was worried I was causing damage.

As sweat started cascading down my face, the doctor added his two cents worth from the peanut gallery, "Try rotating him."

I'm already doing that, thank you very much. Thanks for playing!

In fact, I was driving my hands further inside the woman's vagina and aggressively twisting the kid's slippery body and head, anything I could grab, twisting and rotating to the best of my ability. I didn't care if I inadvertently broke the infant's clavicles and snapped the mother's pubic bone, just as long as I got the kid out.

The situation was rapidly becoming more dangerous because there was not much blood getting to the baby in this crushed position. Finally, the doctor stepped in and together we wrenched out a somewhat blue-hued and floppy kid.

The doctor rushed the newborn over to the recovery station where the nurse was trained in neither obstetrics, nor pediatrics, and certainly not neonatal resuscitation. She didn't even have the correct oxygen line hooked up.

We were on our own out here on the frontier, using cowboy medicine yet again, and I didn't even own a belt-buckle or cowboy hat.

In a bigger hospital setting there would have been several medical teams in the room: neonatologists, pediatricians, nurses—but it was just us: a rural doctor in cowboy boots, a nurse who would be more helpful if she had been offering us cucumber sandwiches, and a petrified resident (that's me) standing in shock, wondering if my attempts to rotate the infant's body in order to dislodge the shoulder had twisted the head 180 degrees, and I had inadvertently snapped the newborn's neck.

At this point, I looked and felt worse than the pale and flaccid infant.

I decided I was dropping out of medicine—I just needed to vomit first. Instead, I swallowed back the bile, and stepped up to help resuscitate the kid.

I didn't see any breaths from the baby as we rubbed his chest, and gently pushed on his abdomen. Then I realized I was going to drop to the floor, absolutely traumatized that I had injured this newborn.

Fortunately, for all of us, he suddenly took a few deep gasps of air; decided he liked oxygen and was perfectly healthy.

I remained in shock for a long, long time.

Over the following years, every single medical student and junior resident working with me on labor and delivery received a very pointed and comprehensive lecture regarding being prepared for shoulder dystocia. Perhaps in some way those lectures, resulting from my own nightmare, have helped protect some mothers and infants elsewhere.

All good things end. It was time to return to work back in the big city, where I had some planned elective rotations on ophthalmology to *look* forward to (silly pun) and had no idea what the fates had lying in store for me (an even sillier, albeit more private pun).

OPHTHALMOLOGY

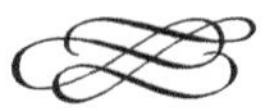

SCOTT RETURNS TO BELLYACHING WHILE YOU SEE A TRUE HERO

Ophthalmology, the treatment of the eyes, is one of the most competitive residency fields. Only super-smart, and super hard-working medical students become ophthalmologists. I did not even consider applying to be an eye doctor; but the eye seemed important to understand and to be able to treat, so, I signed on for an elective month with an ophthalmologist friend of mine, where any patient mistaking me for a super-smart, uber-competitive resident, would rapidly recognize their folly.

Once more I was subjected to a constant barrage of patients taking me aside to tell me what an extraordinary doctor my mentor was to them, how lucky I was to be learning from him, and what an all-around wonderful person he was on top of it all.

Mano was a dear friend. One of the kindest and most caring people in the world, and I considered myself lucky to have coffee with him, let alone be educated in his world of eye care. All those niceties aside, how did I continually work with the super-heroes of the medical world? I felt far less than ordinary, and their non-stop appearances only highlighted my inadequacies.

I was surrounded by wonderful doctors—yet none of their magic was rubbing off on me. Every single patient made it a point to tell me how fortunate he or she was to be treated by Mano. Fortunately for all my future patients with eye issues, I gained some fantastic training for how to properly examine eyes, remove foreign objects and rust rings, and most importantly, where to refer them for advanced care. I also discovered that it was quite fun to see the backs of people's eyes blasted by lasers.

Mano was internationally recognized for his work, and his specialty was managing diabetic retinopathy. Diabetic retinopathy is caused by damage to the blood vessels in the back of the eye, which is where you also find the light receptors that allow you to see. Damage to those blood vessels causes them to leak, which can create scar tissue, which in turn can interfere with vision, pull the retina out of position, and lead to blindness.

So lasers were used to blast the damaged blood vessels around the retina (which is where you find lots of those light receptors for vision).

It has been said that the eye is the window to the soul, and in medicine, the eye really does reflect quite a lot about a person's overall health. In the office, a patient's eyes were dilated—given medicine that made their eye-muscles relax and allowed the pupil to open wide so we could look deep inside with microscopes and assess the health of the blood vessels: were they too straight (hypertension), too pulsatile, leaky (diabetes); were the edges of the optic disc blurry from pressure behind it (glaucoma)? Really amazing, and no, not sure I really saw most of that with my own evaluations, but I could recognize it in an ophthalmology textbook.

What I remember most of my own medical work that month, besides the cute female staff, was the day I watched Mano photograph the blood vessels in his patient's eyes. Dye was injected via an IV into the patient, and the blood vessels in their eyes would light up with the dye so we could snap interesting photographs that I imagine would be fun to look at while taking hallucinogenic mushrooms—something I have never tried, despite the benefits documented for creative work (which would likely have improved this book), not to mention ongoing, groundbreaking work with treating depression, addiction, and other disease states with psilocybin (the psychedelic ingredient in the mushrooms).

Psychedelic discussion over, we again return to ophthalmology and taking photos of colorful patterns of blood vessels in patients' eyes. The nurse assumed, incorrectly, that since I was a doctor, albeit in training, I possessed a modicum of medical skills, like being able to start an IV line. In fact, I was very poorly trained in placing IVs but did not want to dash a nurse's elevated view of my medical prowess.

The first time she asked me to place the IV, I got it in without any problem. Maybe I *was* better than I knew? My poorly timed success however, only further fulfilled her absurd assumption that I knew what I was doing. She asked me to try a difficult IV stick in a different patient. I strutted up to this troublesome patient with tricky veins, poised with both confidence and a large needle, the latter of which I proudly jammed into the back of his hand, performing yet another magnificent IV placement.

"I'll inject when ready," I advised the nurse, and settled back to watch the camera's view of the patient's eyeball. She nodded she was ready, and I injected a large volume of colorful dye.

Instead of watching colorful blood vessels illuminated in artistic waves, I heard the nurse say, "I think there's a—"

And we'll never know what she said after that brilliant opening phrase because her words were rudely muffled by a jarring scream from the patient. Followed by him yelling, "MY HAND! MY HAND!"

I glanced over to look at his hand, which had swollen to the size of a small grapefruit. It was a similar color as well, quite similar to the bright yellow dye I had just injected into his IV, which was apparently misplaced.

Whoops.

Despite my efforts to injure his patients, Mano kept me onboard. Working with him was enjoyable—seeing patients who appreciated the treatment they received from a compassionate physician reminded me that we were actually caring for people. It was easy to be jaded by cynical doctors, working long hours in stressful situations, with little gratitude from the patients for the over and beyond effort that went into every patient's care. But there were also excellent and caring physicians like my friend, who was a hero in his patient's eyes for saving their vision.

All sorts of heroes existed if you looked for them (did you like that segue?). One of the most exciting stories, which should be made part of an *ER* or *Grey's Anatomy* episode, involved a fireball of a resident, nicknamed *the Doberman.*

This surgical resident was one of the best and most caring surgeons anywhere, and struck fear into many students, residents, and nurses. She had to be tough. She was an attractive, ultra-marathon running, 5'1" blond, working in the harsh "old-boy" club of surgery. Her brother had preceded her in the surgical residency program, leaving her in the shadows of one of the most stunning resident reputations to date.

Yours truly happened to be dating her at the time of this incident (same woman who gifted me Winston).

My friend Scott, the one that appeared earlier with a collapsed lung (same guy who had been arrested bungee jumping off the Golden Gate Bridge), was back in the hospital. He had just been operated on for his second collapsed lung (Once is silly, but twice? Come on, twice is downright careless). You might recall the first incident had occurred right before I started residency, and I had missed diagnosing his potentially fatal condition.

This time I received a call from his same girlfriend, Rachel, who had dragged him to the ER to have an X-ray taken because he was complaining and acting grumpy after finishing a 107-mile mountain-bike ride in nine hours. I'm grumpy if I ride my bike around the block without being fed, so I would've assumed anyone crazy enough to ride that far in that much time deserved to be grumpy. In fact, I get grumpy doing almost anything for nine hours.

But Rachel, obviously a far better diagnostician than me, her idiot doctor friend, wisely felt the symptoms were comparable to Scott's previous lung collapse episode. Scott reluctantly agreed to be evaluated in the ER, where they did *eventually* diagnose him with yet another collapsed lung.

My suggestion was that they leave it collapsed to even out the bike-riding field for me; he seemed to ride just fine with one functioning lung, and I needed all the help I could get.

The reason I italicized that he was *eventually* diagnosed was that in the ER, Scott and Rachel had been forced to wait their turn in the triage queue, with Scott feeling short of breath.

What emergency was being triaged ahead of them? Vicki. Vicki was at the front of the ER lineup. Vicki happened to be a frequent flier in the ER, seeking pain pills. Her medical emergency du jour? A bunion flare-up.

Rachel forcefully explained to the ER triage nurse that Scott was having identical symptoms to the last time when he had a completely collapsed lung. Rachel kept requesting that Scott be triaged quickly due to the danger of this likely pneumothorax.

The nurse glanced at Scott, who was breathing without too much difficulty, and assured Rachel that he probably had a bellyache, and that they needed to wait patiently for an X-ray while Vicki was examined first.

That's right, an emergency room team can never underestimate that horrendously precarious ailment, the out-of-control bunion, especially compared to the life-threatening pneumothorax that in the expert eyes of the triage nurse was a bellyache.

So, Vicki was triaged ahead of Scott.

When Scott finally got the requested X-ray, it turned out his lung was *completely* collapsed, yet again—collapsed to the point that it was the size of a brown paper lunch bag if you crushed and crumpled it in your hand. The surgery team was called to evaluate and treat him right away (not for a bellyache)—although I am sure it was difficult prying any of them away from the bunion problem next door.

It's quite possible I just belabored the ER team's overly relaxed attitude to help mitigate my smoldering guilt at missing the same diagnosis one year earlier.

The typical protocol at that point involved the on-call surgery intern for the cardio-thoracic team coming to the ER to evaluate the patient immediately. The current on-call intern, however, preferred spending the evening with his girlfriend, and unwisely opted not to return his pager calls.

Big mistake in general; about to be a lot worse for his ignoring the pager alert to specifically come help the friend of the chief surgical resident, i.e., the Doberman.

Rachel had called me for my support, and far more importantly, to call the dwindling situation's attention to the chief surgical resident (i.e., still the Doberman, also my girlfriend), who could help get something done right away.

The two of us rushed up to the hospital separately. I was worried about Scott. The Doberman was furious that a surgical resident would dare not return multiple pages from the ER.

Instead of the thoracic team taking Scott to surgery that night, as they would have done had the case been properly handled hours earlier, the plan was altered to placing a chest tube (a risky procedure that could have been avoided) and waiting several days to perform the operation (stapling his lung to his chest wall), which would eliminate future lung deflations. Medicine at its finest yet again.

We were met in the ER by the head of the Burn-Trauma surgery department—the same wicked smart, very caring and somewhat terrifying guy from my days as a medical student in the Burn/Trauma ICU. He too was furious with the intern.

I was beginning to seriously fear for the intern's life and felt certain that if he survived his impending lashing, he would undoubtedly be booted from the residency program for shirking his duty (he wasn't).

The trauma surgeon quickly pieced together several crucial tidbits of information: First, the patient was a friend of ours. Being a friend of his chief resident meant something important — things were going to get done immediately. Being a friend of mine meant less than knowing the guy who trimmed his hedges. Secondly, that Scott was a lawyer.

These combined facts seemed to have something to do with his ordering a significantly large dose of Demerol (a narcotic pain medicine) and Versed (an anti-anxiety medicine that also acts as an amnesiac) to be administered prior to the chest tube being placed.

My girlfriend really enjoyed inserting chest tubes, almost pathologically—to the point that I frequently woke up and made sure she hadn't practiced on me during the night. She now delighted in cutting a hole in Scott's side, before ramming a plastic hose into his chest wall. Scott yelled, and then we all heard a rush of air from the tube as his lung re-inflated.

Scott, flying high on amnesia-inducing drugs, then piped in with his two cents: "Have you put the tube in yet?"

We assured him it was indeed in place.

Within a minute of our initial assurances that there was indeed a tube sticking out of his chest, he repeated, "Did you put the tube in yet?" And he continued asking if the tube was in place while being wheeled upstairs into a room.

He continued to perseverate about the tube being in place throughout most of the night, all the way until the medicine wore off; at which point he became extremely aware of the tube being in place.

Scott's lung was eventually stapled to the top of his chest wall to prevent this lung- collapsing nonsense from ever occurring again, and then he sat in the hospital for a few days. Multiple friends visited, bringing gifts to keep him occupied. Scott sat upright in his hospital bed wearing a ripped t-shirt with cigarettes rolled in the sleeve (he does not smoke), an Elmer Fudd-style hunting hat balanced on his head (he does not hunt) and surrounded by a variety of gifted magazines renowned for their literary quality such as *Stuff, Maxim, and Ferret Quarterly (he does not own a ferret),* along with several bottles of alcohol (he does drink). The attending surgeon was not amused.

Nothing too heroic, I know.

I'm merely setting the stage.

A few nights later, on Rachel's birthday, my girlfriend left to pick-up Indian food for us to enjoy in the hospital. She returned to the room a bit late, slightly pale and shaken, and it was only later that I was able to grasp her story in its entirety.

As was her habit, she had called to check in with a surgical nurse to see how each of her patients was doing (this was after she had technically finished for the day and was driving to pick up the food). They were discussing each patient when the nurse stopped to mention that there was a code team outside a room on the sixth floor with a collapsed patient.

My girlfriend quickly realized that it was one of her patient's rooms, then raced back to the hospital, sprinted up six flights of stairs, and dashed onto the sixth floor, where she encountered a chaotic group of people surrounding one of her patients lying unconscious in the hallway.

The internal medicine residents and attending physician running the code were about to shock the unconscious patient because he had no pulse. As we've discussed previously, no pulse is bad.

Suddenly, in the middle of their efforts, and much to everybody's surprise, the 5'1" surgery chief ran up, injected herself into their midst, ordered them to stop, and demanded a pair of scissors.

Nobody moved. The internal medicine attending exploded, wondering who the hell she was and what she was doing. It was his medicine team in charge of the code, and this patient had no pulse. Protocol was shouting for an immediate electric shock to the stalled heart.

Paying little or no attention to his barrage of questions, she grabbed a pair of scissors and now, to everyone's complete and utter shock, cut open the patient right through the surgery wound on his abdomen.

Let me recap in case you don't quite appreciate what's going on: *she cut open a person's abdomen in the middle of the hospital hallway —and then stuck her hand inside the patient!*

When the chairman of surgery came racing down the hall, he found his chief resident on the floor wearing a full-length skirt, with her arm deep inside an unconscious patient, asking, "Is there a pulse yet?"

The furious medical attending was shouting, *"What are you doing? Are you crazy? What are you doing?"*

And she kept calmly asking the nurse, over the barrage of shouts and chaos, "Do you have a pulse yet?"

Suddenly the nurse announced, "We're getting a pulse!"

Which immediately quieted everyone.

Being an astute surgeon, she remembered thinking that the patient's splenic artery had appeared weak when they operated on him. She correctly guessed that the weakened artery had started bleeding, and that his collapsing in the hallway was due to his rapidly losing blood internally. She had clamped the patient's aorta against his spine *with her hand* to stop any further blood loss.

From the sixth-floor hallway the patient was rushed to the O.R. with my girlfriend riding on top of the gurney, pressing her hand against his aorta, keeping the guy from bleeding to death.

She then performed the surgery to complete saving his life.

The guy took a while to recover. Being deprived of blood to the brain had its detriments; when he awoke, he was convinced the 5'1" blond surgeon in the room was his daughter. When he was informed that no, she wasn't his daughter, he apologized, "Sorry, you must be my nurse." That comment, one she heard all too frequently, did not go over well.

To put this somewhat crazy event into perspective, within a day or two, the story became the stuff of legends told throughout surgical residencies across the country—and this was *before* social media sites existed to virally immortalize kitten videos.

Opening a patient in the hallway and using her hands inside the guy to save his life? This feat, treated by her as nothing more than a routine surgical moment, was akin to knocking a grand slam homerun in the ninth inning of the World Series in game seven to win the game—well, something like that. It's what little kid wannabe surgeons would dream of if they cultivated a sense of creativity.

And to be fair, I thought it was an exciting episode, but she was always running off to save lives as a surgeon. The moment however, that finally put this accomplishment into perspective for me occurred when I was having dinner with her brother, the ace of aces surgeon, along with several other all-star surgical resident friends. This was a few weeks later, and without her present.

Eventually their surgery discussions (because that is pretty much all that this group of surgeons discuss when stuck together: surgery, ultra-marathon running, and more surgery) turned to loudly bantering back and forth about the whole event.

They boisterously argued about how much better they would have handled the whole situation, and wished they had been there to save the day instead of her:

"You dream of something like that going down."

"Can you imagine being that lucky?"

"Should have been me."

"Oh man, I would pay to have something like that happen."

All the young surgeons agreed that this was their medical wet dream, being the rebellious action hero, on center stage, in such a grand case, in the middle of the hospital, no less, calmly saving a life in front of everyone with attending physicians yelling at you.

Then there was a moment of silence, total quiet as everyone reflected on the event…

"But you know what?" her brother finally said, looking around at everyone, then shaking his head and chuckling, "I never would have had the balls to do it."

And every single surgeon around the table slowly nodded their head in agreement—they wouldn't have either.

True hero.

Not long after, we both had the weekend off (an unheard-of novelty) and went to the southwest Utah desert to hike with Winston (the dog). We grossly miscalculated our hiking distances, and wound-up hiking around 20 miles each day, quite a bit of which was in water, and without enough food. Nobody said heroes and head-injured people knew how to read maps.

We survived to make it back for the end of the month, where an interesting sequence of events occurred that left both the girlfriend, and my residency program, wishing I had been left in the desert.

INTERMISSION II

WHERE I CRASH MY BIKE AND LAND ON SECRET EXECUTIVE PROBATION

A glorious month of inpatient pediatric medicine, complete with small patients, new drugs, and busy call schedule, awaited me. But first, I had a wedding to attend. Over the previous months I had spoken with the pediatric chief resident (who oversaw our schedules), requesting the rotation's first weekend off so I could attend this important wedding in New York. Scott (of the deflating lungs) and I were to be *"Bridesmen"* for Katie, a woman we considered akin to a little sister—although, truth be told, she was far more mature and wiser than the two of us put together.

It was Katie's brother, John, who had died in a car accident during my third year of medical school. Katie had requested that Scott and I walk her mother down the aisle. There was no question that I would be present with the family for this momentous event, the first real occasion they were going to let themselves celebrate since John's accident.

Regarding my request for the weekend off, the pediatric chief resident repeatedly told me, "No problem, just remind me when we get closer to the actual date."

After his many assurances that I was excused for the weekend, I booked my plane ticket. But I called him every few weeks thereafter to remind him of my planned absence. And he kept telling me, "No problem, just remind me when it's closer."

And the date kept getting closer, until it was the week I was leaving—and for the first time, he stopped answering my calls.

Then it was even closer, as in, it was the night I was flying out. I planned to board a red eye flight to New York at 11:55 that evening. And the children's hospital, for all I knew, expected me to round on patients the following morning.

I telephoned the chief resident over and over, but still, he didn't answer. I kept calling, leaving messages at his home, at the hospital, on his pager, "Hi, this is John, remember how you asked me to remind you when we're closer to the weekend I needed off, well, we're close, I'm leaving tonight...Ok, hope I hear from you."

I never heard back.

I then made two assumptions (both wrong):

1) Since I had communicated with him so many times over the last months about my request to be away for the approaching weekend and had stalked him with reminders throughout the day, he had already sent the approval to the hospital, and I had nothing to worry about.

2) I would be able to stop by his house that evening, knock on his door, and personally confirm that he had approved my absence for the weekend and had already let the hospital know.

Then, for those of you wondering why there's no mention of any bike crashes yet, I decided to enter a bike race that evening.

Why, oh why, do you still even contemplate getting on a bike? Good question. Because it's fun?

That very night, the same night I was scheduled to leave for the wedding and planned to stop by the pediatric chief's house, I raced in a criterium (crit) bike race. A crit involves a hundred cyclists racing around a track for an hour.

The race was going great. A group of five riders had broken

from the main pack and built a substantial lead. My teammates were sitting in front of the main group controlling the pace, and I decided to sprint up to the break group while the main pack was held back—stick with me just a touch longer, this does have medical relevance.

I managed to catch the break group and felt strong going into the final sprint. I was perfectly positioned behind the lead-out rider. As we stood and started sprinting towards the finish, taking the speeds up to over 30 miles per hour, an adjacent racer tried sliding between the lead out rider and myself—in doing so, his rear wheel clipped my front wheel, spinning it sideways. I still have the horrible image imprinted on my brain, watching my front wheel spin 90 degrees at high speed.

I was instantly slammed onto the asphalt racetrack—more like splatted and skidded. Then two more cyclists landed on top of me for a 100-foot-long slide down the road.

I later learned that the race officials had immediately called an ambulance as nobody thought I would get up. But I sprang to my feet, bleeding from my shoulders, legs, thighs, back and hip. My helmet was cracked from where my head had smashed onto the track; my bike wheels were bent, my jersey had holes burned through it, and my bike pedal was two-thirds its original size, having been ground down by the asphalt track.

Having a concussion yet again, and being covered in road rash, was no way to go through life. However, that night I needed to get on the red eye flight across country, say hello to my mother who lived in New York City, and then head to the wedding—there was no time for philosophical reflection.

I was driven home from the race and dropped at my girlfriend's house—the surgical chief resident. She had very little empathy regarding my inability to stay on a bike and scrubbed the wounds mercilessly. Never go to a surgeon if you want compassion.

Medically I was slightly concerned that, once again, I might have a small bleed in my brain as I had a terrible headache and was perseverating (loudly repeating the same questions and statements), both signs of concussion. With my thinking blurred, I pondered three hazy fears:

1) *If* I had a bleed in my head, and I was flying at altitude, would the pressure increase the amount of blood I was losing, and would I then die on the flight?

2) I was supposed to wear a tuxedo and currently had bloody road rash over my entire body.

3) I would, not for the first or last time, need to face my mother and tell her I had been in yet another bike accident. Those were my current fears, fears soon to be surpassed by far more relevant ones.

Looking back, I suspect the residency would like me to mention that I was concerned about not having my responsibilities at the pediatric hospital properly covered. But I was barely putting rational thoughts together.

For an entire night, thanks to the concussion, I think I literally forgot I was remotely involved in the field of medicine. I certainly forgot to stop by the pediatric chief's house. Maybe it was a subconscious relief valve, or maybe I figured the pediatric chief resident must have heard one the many messages I had left for him in various locations. The concerning facts that I had attained neither formal confirmation to take the weekend off, nor secured someone to cover the following morning's shift for me in the hospital had completely deserted my mind. I was essentially abandoning my responsibilities; except I didn't really remember.

Either way, a few hours later I was bandaged and flying across country with both a concussion and a plan, and I'm not sure which was the worse of the two.

My plan? For the possible brain bleed fear, I decided that if I started to feel loopy flying across country, I would hyperventilate into a paper bag to reduce my head pressure, and drink alcohol during the flight to slow my metabolism. I am not sure if the second part of that plan was medically legitimate, but I was doing my best to think rationally through a concussion.

Fear #2, wearing clothes (including a tuxedo) over road rash, was addressed by purchasing copious amounts of gauze and salve. Easy.

I did not typically tell my mother when I was involved in accidents. But in this unavoidable face-to-face situation (fear #3), she would want to give me a hug, and I would start grimacing and crying from pain if she did. Instead, I just limped back from her approaching embrace and spilled my explanation—avoiding both the painful hug and her likely knee-jerk reaction to knock some sense into me for playing silly games at my age.

My residency program, however, was furious (understatement). I sat on a park bench receiving a vicious tongue lashing over the phone from a senior family practice resident about me being an irresponsible deserter. The program director vented how embarrassing it was for the family practice department to receive a phone call from the pediatric department regarding an assigned resident not showing up in the hospital that morning.

The family practice chief resident scrambled to find another resident to work for me, so the shift was covered. I however remained in a remarkable spot of bother. I would be expected to show up in the department office to discuss the weighty repercussions upon my return.

"I'm scheduled to be on call when I get back, do you want me to miss another day at the hospital?"

Total silence which I correctly interpreted as them trying to figure a way to kill me over the phone line.

"Show up as soon as you're off call."

"I have clinic that afternoon."

I could feel hot anger pulsing through the phone.

"As soon as clinic ends."

I'll repeat, I was in serious trouble. Although I was having a difficult time understanding the level of heat being fired my direction. I had been granted leave to be absent (albeit an unconfirmed claim) and my work had been covered. Apparently, I had trodden on some peace accord between the family practice and pediatric departments.

And notice how nobody batted an eyelash about a resident being scheduled for a 36-hour work shift. Upon my return I would be on-call overnight in the hospital without sleep, then chastised, punished, and likely kicked out of my residency program. Which meant one thing, I needed to have a *lot* of fun before then.

I'll discuss the residency fallout soon enough after relaying key parts of the wedding. I put my concussion and injuries on hold, took some excruciating showers, wrapped my body in gauze, numbed the pain with cocktails, and rejoiced wholeheartedly.

Most importantly, the wedding weekend was beautiful and poignant. We visited the site where John was buried and cried. Then, for the rest of the weekend, we celebrated and danced and feasted, all of which somehow led to me waking up in a poolhouse with a bridesmaid and looking out to see the caterers setting up a post-wedding night brunch.

Three hundred people were about to arrive for brunch and two people would still be in tuxedo and bridesmaid dress—their own, respectively.

This semi-platonic mistake (we had kissed) would be mildly scandalous as the bridesmaid was not my girlfriend.

(Side note: nobody can steal that for screenplay material, as I've already written it into a film script, and the scene was performed wonderfully at the London Screenwriters Festival.)

On the shameful downside, I could now, thanks to my poor decision-making skills, add one more person to the growing list of people who might kill me upon my return. On the mild upside, the wedding had mostly helped me forget the mean-spirited telephone call with my residency program.

I had survived that one miserable conversation with our program's chief resident and program director, and later discovered that the chief of pediatrics, the one I had called repeatedly, had been out of town—and being out of town meant he was unavailable to corroborate my concussive insistencies that he had agreed to let me off for the weekend.

I was therefore still in trouble with charges of going AWOL.

I'd like to blame the residency causing me sufficient stress to drive me to drink copious amounts of gin and celebrate quite hard without sleep—but at some point, I needed to be accountable for my actions. And that time was now. Despite looking for alternatives, I boarded the return flight to my unpleasant reality.

I flew home hung-over, exhausted, not feeling altogether good about much of anything. Arriving home late, I confessed to my girlfriend about the pool-house incident, which resulted in our staying up and talking through the night. Which was completely my fault. Seeing the hurt I caused someone I cared about was infinitely worse than facing the anger spewing from the residency program. For reasons I'm sure a psychologist could best explain, when one aspect of life was burning up, why not sabotage others?

I was going to be on call in the pediatric hospital starting the following morning and likely staying awake all night yet again. I would work in the hospital the following day until dragging myself to work in my clinic, and finally I would trudge to the family practice department office where I would likely be executed on charges of desertion. If I could stay awake.

INPATIENT PEDIATRICS —LAHEY TEAM

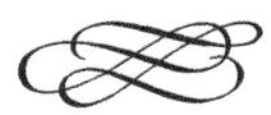

WHAT TO DO WHEN TEAM WYOMING DISAPPEARS (YET AGAIN)

My final intern rotation was another inpatient pediatric stint at the children's hospital. It felt quite apropos to be back working in pediatrics; the Children's hospital stocked cookies on every hallway corner and had video games in play areas for the little patients. I would be right at home because during the last four days I had smashed everyone's belief that I could act like a responsible adult.

Fortunately, in comparison to the previous evening's showdown with my girlfriend, and my residency program's somewhat harsh scolding, my arrival on the pediatric team (where I was also in trouble for having not shown up the previous Friday) was relatively pain-free. Although, during the ensuing 48 hours, still swathed in gauze, I turned every corner with heightened anxiety, waiting to be yelled at, struck with a pipe, or made to feel small and irresponsible.

The pediatric team made a few jokes and then dropped the whole incident (remember, people who work in pediatric care are inherently nice people). And finally, with altogether piss-poor timing, the previously absent pediatric chief resident popped his head into our morning rounds, laughed, and informed the pediatric department that I had indeed been granted the time off, and was not in any trouble at all—at least not with them. Bit of a tardy appearance on his part, which did nothing at all to mollify the family practice program's fury.

The family practice residency program, always so zippity-doodah chock full of themselves promoting good listening as the key to being a good doctor, *refused* to listen to the pediatric chief resident. I was still enemy number one—no, make that idiot number one in their eyes.

Meanwhile, I was set to spend that day and night working in the pediatric hospital. That is, if I could stay awake for what would likely be my fifth relatively sleepless night in a row. I could then look forward to facing the rage of the residency program the following day when I was to appear in front of the Family Practice director for disciplinary actions.

Ironically, every other member on my pediatric team ended up needing more days off than I had missed (I had only missed one day and night for the wedding). The Director of the Family Practice program, however, was far from pleased. I presented my case yet again, explaining the odd circumstances of what had transpired with the bike crash, that I had made efforts for months and received permission to be absent that weekend, and that the pediatric chief would corroborate my story. But these points were all irrelevant to the director, who was concerned with one fact: I was a no-show for my rotation duty, had not found someone to cover my shift, all of which resulted in his receiving that embarrassing call about my absence, which reflected poorly on his program.

To put this story to an end, I was made to later appear before a sort of mock trial court to plead my case. On yet another post-call, tired afternoon, I stood, head hung low, in front of a table of sneering family practice department heads and disgusted senior residents to rehash how irresponsible I was, and to not listen to my worthless excuses.

I was ordered to write several letters of contrition to the family practice and pediatric departments.

I was then placed on Secret Executive Probation.

I'm not kidding.

I did not want to be in residency, and it seemed nobody else did at that point either.

For the next years I was on probation, to be promptly excused from the residency program if I screwed up again. Odds were increasingly stacked against my finishing residency. The "secret" part of the probation was that they would not place this troublesome episode in my file unless I was eventually given the boot.

And amidst the self-inflicted debacles, I was still an accepted member of the pediatric Lahey team.

Maybe I should transfer to pediatrics, at least they were nice to me.

LET'S GET BACK TO PRACTICING MEDICINE. FOR THIS ROTATION I WAS on the "Lahey" team, which cared for all the pediatric oncology (cancer) patients. This service terrified me. As if being unsure from which direction a dagger might fly at me during those days wasn't enough to kill my appetite, I now faced the added stress of working on a pediatric oncology team.

Why was I stressed? Let's start with what I knew about pediatric oncology:

Nothing.

Zero.

Less than that.

My imposter syndrome flew down and slapped me silly about my traumatized head, several times. I was certain every other resident had clearly memorized oncology treatment protocols in medical school while I was sleeping off my concussions and drooling on my desk.

I wanted to be a struggling actor and planned on funding that financially idiotic endeavor by working part time in a ski town's medical clinic. I admit, my plan had several flaws, but when would I ever, possibly, order chemotherapy medicines to treat a kid with cancer?

Never.

Not ever.

Not to mention that my behavior and intentions clearly indicated that I was not responsible enough to deal with myself, my relationships, bicycling or being an adult, *let alone* dealing with vulnerable child cancer patients and their cancer-killing drugs.

I didn't even know the names of cancer-killing medications, let alone their uses, dangers, or how to dose a kid just enough to poison a tumor, but not kill the patient.

Couldn't I just go home and hide under my bed until the storm abated? If I stayed there until the month ended, nobody would realize I was a massive hospital liability.

Those were my defensive thoughts as I crossed the threshold into the children's hospital. Fortunately, the pediatric team as mentioned, laughed (at me), and welcomed me to the team.

Then, after the initial jokes, we got down to the serious business at hand: I was not to receive any food cards, yet again. Turns out, nobody was concerned about what the residents knew regarding oncology medication regimens; what mattered most was that there were no food cards for me. See what I mean, pediatric people are super caring, they were worried about my wellbeing. Food cards were paper money we were given to pay for meals at the children's hospital cafeteria. Without those cards, I could not afford to eat. I was broke, and I was on call, meaning, I would not be able to eat until the next day at home. I was going to starve.

I'm being melodramatic, I was not going to starve. I was going to steal cookies from the kid's snack trays and be fine. Ironically, for the first time in many days, the reason I was being denied food cards had nothing to do with me doing anything wrong.

Remember my last stint on the pediatric service, when I had thirty charts left by a resident from Wyoming? Here, once again, were charts left for me by an absent resident.

I was informed that the previous family practice resident on the team had left the program (he'd apparently jumped the last stagecoach back to—you guessed it—Wyoming) without dictating seventeen charts. And for some pigheaded reason derived from a medieval legal writ regarding Family Practice residents being responsible for covering their doltish brethren's work, I would not be handed any food cards until those charts were completed.

What in the name of mangy moose turds was wrong with these residents from Wyoming? They consistently left their charts for me to dictate. Perhaps they were due back for some cow-roping competition? Whatever the lame belt-buckle shining excuse, I was left with the extra workload *and* without any meal tickets.

Fortunately, starvation wasn't a huge problem in the children's hospital. I could live off the sugar-laden snack carts that elves magically delivered on the hour. Even better, a very cute female resident on the team slipped me a handful of food cards after hazing me for not showing up the previous Friday. Things were looking up, at least in terms of eating.

Famine issues resolved; I could now tune into practicing medicine on our morning rounds. As rounds progressed, my stress levels further abated. I discovered that the Oncology attending physician ordered all the crazy chemotherapy cocktails and did not expect us to start creatively ordering poisonous potions. In fact, I'm quite certain that the real doctors preferred we family practice types stayed far away from any attempts at ordering chemotherapy drugs.

Instead, we were expected to care for the oncology patients admitted to the hospital by monitoring their vitals and watching for physical signs of illness or adverse medicine effects.

These patient's immune systems were often decreased as a side effect of their chemo treatments, which meant they became sick quite easily, and any infections were very dangerous as their depleted bodies had a hard time fighting off illness.

Parents returned to the hospital whenever their young and tough oncology patient children developed any signs of infection, such as a fever. These poor parents absolutely dreaded fevers.

When a child being treated for cancer was admitted with a fever, we followed protocols to identify the likely site of infection with lots of lab tests, and aggressively treated the patients with multiple strong antibiotics. For the next days we carefully monitored the patient's temperatures and white blood cell counts to see if the antibiotic treatments were effective so that the parents could breathe a sigh of relief, and their children could return home.

You could see the fear in those parents' eyes—fear that their weakened child was dangerously sick; they were constantly fearing for their child's survival.

The kids, meanwhile, donning hospital gowns and often sporting bald heads as a side-effect from chemotherapy, ran around the halls, dragging their IV poles, looking for treats, playrooms, and video game play stations. Despite my fear of not knowing what to do on an oncology team, the routine was essentially the same: round on patients, write notes, and eat whenever possible.

If anything, our role in the treatment of pediatric oncology patients was straightforward because the tricky parts were handled by the attending physicians, and the care we delivered was mostly protocol based. Machines and monkeys could follow the protocols as effectively as me—although, likely without displaying my typical expression of mixed-up muddledness. And they would certainly have a hard time dictating old charts with the same level of derision, loathing, and sarcasm I poured into finishing those abandoned charts from the bison turd-head residents from Wyoming.

While we were responsible for the oncology patients, we also cared for all the other patients that were admitted into the hospital on our call nights. Patients with heart problems were transferred to the Veasey team, and then we shared all the other admitted patients between us. So, we admitted and cared for kids with diabetes, bellyaches, pneumonia, sickle cell anemia, whatever showed up. Being in a children's hospital, therefore, also meant we also cared for kids who were the victims of Non-Accidental Trauma (NAT), child abuse.

Physicians in a pediatric hospital really love kids, and part of their responsibility is confronting suspected cases of abuse—accidental or otherwise. My initial reaction, when shown photographs of shaken babies or injured kids, was to go knock the teeth out of the guilty adult's head.

One of the attending doctors calmly explained to me that they all had to face the reality that oftentimes parents reacted against their kids without thinking. After a stressful day, with various frustrations—at their job, finances, or just *life*—and facing kids who are acting like kids, they acted out inappropriately. And the best thing, for all involved, was to admit the parent into an anger management course, not to knock their teeth out.

It was still hard to stomach.

Sadly, NAT is something that doctors must constantly consider when they see young patients with injuries—be it bruises, fractures, or even emotional changes. It might sound reasonable to think that an occasional case would appear with an injury that did not match the explanation. Unfortunately, NAT was a more common occurrence than we wished, and was not straightforward to recognize. Sometimes the radiologist or orthopedic doctor tipped you off that an injury might be suspicious, as there was radiological evidence of previous injuries fitting with NAT.

The state of Utah made it a doctor's responsibility to report *all* suspected cases of NAT; the idea being to relieve doctors of the burden of deciding to report something or not. It is really difficult to confront a parent if you suspect NAT. Imagine a parent bringing their child into an ER for a swollen bruise on their head from falling down the stairs—and let's make it a relatively uncomplicated example, the bruise looks a day or two old, but the parent says it just happened today, and the child has been drowsy ever since. And you notice a few bruises on the child's arm. What do you do?

In that case, you probably ask the parent if they are certain about the timing, as the bruise looks yellow, usually a sign of an old injury. Then the attending ER physician would be the one to confront the parent and take the pressure off an intern. There were still times you had to take a deep breath and ask probing questions of the adults to find out about other injuries or a history of trauma.

And you could feel anger swelling inside the room, and you had to put it away. What if you were wrong and there was no abuse? What would you do to help this child? And now, having my own children, just writing these paragraphs reduces me to tears, remembering those kids I treated over the years.

And most cases were difficult to identify, such as listening to an over-caring adult who seemed genuinely nervous about their child's wellbeing. One who seems so concerned that their otherwise healthy young kid has a broken arm—but the child just won't make appropriate eye contact in the exam room... something nags at you, it just doesn't seem right...well, according to the law, you were right to question the parent; but it's awkward to confront a parent with those suspicions.

But we did confront them (and do) any time we're concerned. I've had adults start yelling at me and walk out of the clinic; I've had parents take a deep breath and admit it was an accident, they struck out at the child, and were genuinely embarrassed and contrite and willing to get help, even it was a one-time incident. I would say most doctors develop a pretty accurate instinct when a case does not sound or feel right, like having a sixth sense when it comes to identifying narcotic-seeking patients. And then there are times when you did not have to trust instinct, and instead just had to keep a calm head.

Late one night in the hospital we received word that two brothers were being admitted to our care. They had been locked in a basement and strapped to a mattress for several months. We did not receive a lot of details on how the boys' horrific situation had been exposed; but learned that their own aunt and uncle, their legal guardians, had been taken into custody. With anger, compassion, disgust all raging in my head, I entered the patient room to meet and examine these boys.

They were malnourished and had suffered multiple forms of abuse. Not sure what to expect, I remember being most affected by how polite the elder brother, an emaciated teenage boy with lanky bones pressing out against his pale skin, was as I questioned and examined him. Working with so many people who worked ridiculous hours to help kids, it was an unbearable contrast to realize we also lived in a society where people with similar DNA, perhaps harboring their own traumatic histories, were capable of such heinous actions. But our job that night was to care for the boys, not deal with the abusers.

There are times in medicine which require you keep your emotions in check to objectively complete your required work without distraction. That's how I recall handling the case, very gently, and objectively, careful to treat these boys like any other patient, without undo sympathy. How could you otherwise function in cases like this which brutally kick you in the gut?

AND THAT MY READERS, WAS THE END OF MY FIRST YEAR OF residency. Two to go, and if they were anything like my first, I wasn't certain I was going to survive.

The truth, as mentioned earlier, was that I never planned to complete the next years. All along, my plan was to leave, now. But then the program almost kicked me out (for missing that pediatrics shift)—and my ego prevented me from doing what they'd threatened to do.

On top of which I discovered that my plan had several strategic flaws. If I left, I would immediately be responsible for my medical school loan payments, which meant I would need to work a lot of hours. Secondly, nobody really wants to hire an M.D. with one year of intern training, even for part-time shift work. You just don't know what you're doing yet. So, my plan was complete shyte. I needed more training, and I needed to prove I could finish for the sake of my self-confidence.

I decided to continue residency without telling anyone about my internal struggles.

As far as residency was concerned, nothing changed, the calendar page flipped, and we all started our next rotation with zero fanfare.

PULMONARY TEAM

"YOU CAN'T REALLY DUST FOR VOMIT." – NIGEL TUFNEL, SPINAL TAP

Second-year residents, just like second-year medical students, loved telling new interns (and students respectively), "The best thing about second year? Not being a first-year."

And I should know how much better because I was a second-year resident. No more suffering as an "intern" with long hours of grunt work, terrible call schedules, without even the recognition of being called a resident.

Except, I screwed up. I never did all my intern requirements.

I had opted to postpone many difficult rotations during my intern year, falsely believing I would avoid them by not continuing residency. My dreamy thespian bubble now burst, I faced the repercussions of starting my second year on a required, month-long service of inpatient medicine at the University Hospital. I would be working with all the brand-new interns as one of their equals.

For the entire month, I was forced to endure one person after another shaking their head and telling me, "I remember how bad it was being an intern. Good luck, just one year to go."

After correcting the first hundred smug well-wishers with, "I know, I'm a second-year too," I started smiling and just thinking, *thank you, now piss off, I know what I'm doing.*

Beyond speechless guile, my advantage was experience. Having one year of working the system under my scrub-ties made me far more efficient than the other interns. Suddenly, the advantage of being at the University Hospital, where few people knew I really was a second- year in disguise as an intern, appeared brightly to me. These people were unwittingly impressed with how quickly I learned to work as an intern and were also willing to forgive any mistakes due to my supposedly being on the first ever month of residency training. *Who was I to correct their assumptions?* For the first time ever as a resident, I was able to relax (a bit), and started enjoying my time on an inpatient service (slightly), because I knew what I was doing (kind of), and we had a fun team (we did).

On one of our first mornings together, we entered a patient room to evaluate a young man with aspiration pneumonia. Aspiration pneumonia occurs when someone inhales food into his or her lungs. This embarrassing gastronomic faux pas was typically reserved for the elderly, or mentally impaired (congenitally or otherwise, such as being stupid drunk).

That morning, upon learning that our patient had developed pneumonia after getting drunk, passing out, vomiting, and inhaling said vomit into his lungs, I turned to my senior resident (who also happened to be a second-year resident, just like myself) and served up the line, "Do you think we could dust for vomit?"

Such cult classic film references, this one from Rob Reiner's brilliant rockumentary, *Spinal Tap, (Footnote:* I would actually meet Rob Reiner, one of the nicest people ever, years later, and as compared to dealing with a patient with a heart attack, where I remained calm and at ease, I was a sweaty, smitten, rambling mess) would have been met with blank stares in my provincial, community hospital-based program just down the road; but in this larger, more culturally adroit atmosphere, the chief promptly mimicked a

British accent in return, volleying, "No, no, you can't really dust for vomit, can you?"

It quickly became accepted that everyone on the team was expected to have a working knowledge of *Spinal Tap* and *Monty Python* quotations to survive the month together.

Among the many highlights of that month (beyond chanting, "Run away! Run away!" as we futilely attempted to escape rooms reeking of various bodily fluids) was the honor of caring for the patient with the distinction of being the longest surviving individual with total lung transplants.

He was a surly, thirty-nine-year-old pain in the ass who had recently suffered a bad turn of health and was downright pissed-off twenty-seven hours a day. And after surviving twenty years with bilateral lung transplants, he would selfishly die under my watch.

Our team, the pulmonary team, had been gifted responsibility for his medical care due to his many lung complications. He was currently in the hospital with a nasty infection that had rotted away the flesh on one of his legs. His hip now fell wide open like a hock of ham.

His family informed us that he had been quite happy until this recent infection made it impossible for him to walk. I had to agree, losing the ability to walk was a legitimate reason to be extremely grumpy. Our role in his care consisted of doing paperwork and guessing which mixture of antibiotics to try for his many circulating, medically resistant, infections.

Each antibiotic cocktail we prescribed for him came with a different series of side effects, one being a terrible case of diarrhea due to Clostridium Dificile (C.Diff). Antibiotics often wiped-out good bacteria in a patient's intestines, which left room for dangerous bacteria to proliferate in their place.

C.Diff was one such "bad" bacteria—it caused green slime to grow in an infected patient's intestines, triggering a constant stream of bloody diarrhea. Ironically, the treatment for this opportunistic bacterial overgrowth, which had resulted from the use of antibiotics, was to prescribe more antibiotics—none of which worked too well.

Currently the rates of resistant C. Diff infections (i.e. infections that do not respond to antibiotics) have skyrocketed in hospitals, and the latest treatment du jour? Fecal transplants. Just like it sounds, you get someone else's poop injected up into your intestines to counter the bacteria imbalance.

What a shitty mess.

Meanwhile, back to the medical wonder who had survived twenty years with lung transplants. The poor guy's situation just kept deteriorating: his leg infection worsened, the infection started to spread throughout his body, and now, bedridden, he was forced to contend with a continual stream of diarrhea thanks to our prescribing multiple courses of antibiotics.

The surgery team was eventually called in to discuss amputating his infected, and now necrotic, leg—an option the cantankerous patient vehemently refused.

We abided by his refusal until he was pretty much unconscious from the infection triggering sepsis—a nasty complication from an infection that causes a chemical reaction to overwhelm the body; think total body infection. His family finally agreed we should amputate the diseased leg to save his life.

So, the surgeons amputated his necrotic leg that was the source of the infection and was now causing life-threatening sepsis. Typically, if you can eliminate the source of disease, the body can heal.

The infections, however, already flowing through his body, continued to worsen after the amputation—likely due to his delaying the decision to amputate in the first place. He was now, and understandably so, an even worse cussing sourpuss to face every day.

Late one morning, as I procrastinated facing his slur of malcontented comments, I was beckoned to hurry to his room by the overhead pager calling a code alert.

The surgery team had by now taken over most of his care, and my work consisted of saying hello, being spat at, and signing the medical team notes agreeing with whatever the surgery team had ordered for his daily treatment plan.

I raced to the patient's room, where the surgery intern, who had been a doctor for less than a month, was drenched in sweat because he had ordered too large a sedative dose for the patient. The patient had coded (stopped breathing), and the surgical intern was now convinced he had killed him.

As we proceeded with the code, I could tell the intern was really beating himself up, standing aside, perspiring heavily. It was probably the first patient to die under his care. The patient, only thirty-nine years old, died in front of us. He had been dying for months.

The tearful surgical intern, with ghostly pallor, stumbled into the hall. He was going to experience a really miserable and unforgettable surgical morbidity and mortality conference. And he has hopefully never, ever, miscalculated a dose of medicine again. Maybe his math skills suck and he has. I don't know.

Two important lessons from my intern year that I already wrote about: 1) Mistakes happen. 2) Sick patients rarely survive real code events in the hospital.

While the patients and surgeons I encountered were having a rough start to their new residency life, I was relatively happy. Our team was working a notoriously miserable rotation together, and for one of the first times, I felt a sense of team camaraderie—using our humor to get through the long days.

We needed this humor because we were the pulmonary service, and the pulmonary service had the dubious honor of accepting the care of all patients with any lung problems—of which there are ample numbers in the hospital. Almost every patient transferred out of the ICU (inherently complicated patients) had a lung problem because they had all recently been intubated, so we welcomed them to join our service with open arms.

Family practice residents were not even supposed to be on the pulmonary team because working in the world as a "general practitioner" meant that you would never be faced with treating such specific lung problems—essentially the month could be better spent with some potentially useful and relevant learning. However, as the scourge of the residency system, we family practice residents were occasionally stuck there as a source of labor to fill in when one of the internal medicine residents decided they wanted to transfer off it.

There were four teams on the internal medicine service at this hospital, and they rotated call nights. The other teams accepted new patients when they were on call. We accepted them on our call nights, as well as accepting any patient with lung problems regardless of what day they decided to get sick, or to be transferred to the floor from the ICU.

Additionally, if you were an internal medicine resident, you were excused from working in your clinic during this pulmonary team rotation. But not so for us dopey Family Practice people. As usual we were expected to show up in our clinic when we weren't on-call. I should stop being upset about the hours; it was an effective and glorious opportunity to see more patients and practice medicine. And sticking a fork in your eye is a good way to see if it's sharp.

Even through optimistic lenses, the hours were long and painful. I would stay up all night on call, then start writing notes on my patients at 4:30 a.m. to get an early start, knowing I had to be at clinic that afternoon.

The patients loved our early exams.

"How was your night Mr. Wilson?"

"It's still dark out."

"Rise and shine buddy, rise and shine."

I would deal with orders and rounding through the morning, and a false sense of hope would start to glimmer, that I would make it to clinic on time.

Then the Chief Resident would shatter my dream: "Guess what, you need to go work up three new patients being transferred out of the ICU, sorry."

"You know I have to be in clinic in forty-five minutes?"

"Well, uh, write fast."

How good do you think the care is for three patients that I had to evaluate, read through all their ICU chart notes, do an exam, and write transfer orders—which included all the medicines they were supposed to survive on—when I had forty-five minutes before I was supposed to be in clinic? Not the best is the right answer. But if they survived another night, I could fix things in the morning.

Not to mention, if you added the hours between starting at around 6 a.m. one morning and finishing at clinic around 6 p.m. the following night, we routinely worked thirty-six-hour shifts. Now, what if you tried telling your residency program that they were exceeding the "allowable" hours for a resident? They would argue back that you had a Saturday off the previous weekend that averaged out to practically a week of vacation time over the month, and that you would be docked that time if you didn't shut up.

The only way to survive such nonsense was to fall back on *Spinal Tap*. There were lots of lines from that film that applied to hospital life beyond "dusting for vomit," such as the "fine line between stupid and clever."

ONE SERVICE REQUIREMENT DURING THE MONTH WAS TO PRESENT A case during morning conference. To properly present a case, a resident would take an "exciting" new patient admitted during their call night and research that patient's presenting disease. They would gather all the lab and radiology results, and then present the case to the other residents, medical students, and an attending physician during morning conference.

The chief resident would proctor the whole thing as the entire group worked through the patient as though encountering him or her for the first time. The person presenting was supposed to have all the answers and be able to teach the group about the case. It was normally a relaxed atmosphere with low attendance, as people were working, and only interns and medical students were required to attend. I didn't think I had anything to teach all the smart people surrounding me, and instead hoped we would somehow finish the rotation before I was forced to embarrass myself.

Eventually, however, my number came up—I needed to present a case. I happened to admit a patient that night with a strange infection that we brilliant residents diagnosed, against suspicions, as an opportunistic infection due to the patient's yet undiagnosed HIV, which we uncovered. It was a great case, and we were extremely proud of ourselves for figuring it out.

I had all the details ready for my presentation, had looked up several articles on the subject, and hoped the attending would help teach part of the case because they liked to show off their superior knowledge (recall Rule B: doctors want to look cool).

I was slightly late for conference that morning, as I was gathering the patient's X-rays. When I finally walked into the teaching room, I discovered the conference room was packed tight, standing room only, with an excited buzz permeating the stifled air. Had people learned of my exciting presentation? Were they turning out to support me, their favorite intern? Unsurprisingly the answer to both questions was "No."

The correct answer was that the Chairman of the Internal Medicine department was attending our morning conference. As though his dogmatic presence would not be intimidating enough, he brought with him the co-authors of a book he had published, a book used by doctors and residents all around the nation, *The Sanford Guide to Antimicrobial Therapy.*

This book, *The Sanford Guide,* is *the* guideline we all used for treating infectious diseases. The authors of this bible of infectious disease treatments, as you might therefore suspect, had a slightly stronger knowledge base of infectious diseases than most inanimate objects, all residents, for that matter, and certainly me.

Does the significance of what I just said fill you with sympathetic nausea? Within several minutes I was going to stand in front of a steamy packed house and attempt to give an educational presentation on "infection" to arguably the world's leading authorities on infection. This almost comical moment devised by some humorous scheduling gods was similar to a preschooler endeavoring to educate NASA scientists about rocket propulsion. I was about to confirm all suspicions that I was indeed the resident simpleton.

Let me turn the heat up a little bit more. I was not just presenting any old infection, but HIV. Our new Chairman of Internal Medicine, Merle Sande, M.D., the book's namesake, had moved from the San Francisco Bay Area, where he had been a preeminent expert on HIV/AIDS. He was internationally considered a *GIANT* in the world of medicine. At that precise moment it seemed completely plausible that I would not have to feign a panic attack, nor pretend to pass out, as either seemed imminent. Fortunately, I had not had time to eat, or I would have preceded that panic attack by vomiting in front of everyone present.

The situation was all too similar to one of my worst University experiences ever, when I had been scheduled to present my thesis on the Cuban Missile Crisis to my International Relations class. The professor that day had coincidentally decided to skip ahead of his syllabus and taught the same subject--and much to my chagrin, presented an almost identical thesis to mine. Then two students presented ahead of me, and both had somehow chosen the exact same thesis. One of them even happened to have had Thanksgiving dinner with Robert McNamara (The U.S. Secretary of Defense during the crisis) the week before and used him for real life footnotes on the subject.

If not for the similarly divine sense of comedy, the situation was horrific. By the time the class had heard the same thesis for the fourth time in one afternoon, they had given up trying to appear interested, and lay snoring on their desks, while I fumbled and murmured through my notes trying to find anything unique to add, but instead kept apologizing for disturbing anyone's respite.

And this morning was sure to be much worse. I have very little recall of the actual presentation beyond the sound of my pounding heart in the hot and crowded room. I glanced over at my senior resident, who was supportively trying to suppress his laughter. He sympathetically shook his head, and mouthed some encouraging words from *Spinal Tap*: "Do you feel like a preserved moose?"

I laughed, nodding my head, and relaxed into my totally screwed state of affairs. I cleared my throat and started the presentation, my voice disappearing into that of a pre-pubescent schoolgirl's: "A forty-three-year-old male, previously healthy, presented last night..."

If I remember correctly, the Nation's infectious disease experts figured out my tricky case in seven seconds flat, kind of like a first-round knockout; they then took over debating the topic amongst themselves while I stupidly stood bobbing my head in agreement. Fortunately my post-call brain, often a body unto itself, did nothing flippant, like piping up to disagree with the infectious disease guideline's authors. I just stood mutely perspiring.

The month turned out to be quite long. Thirty-one days long, in fact, just like every other July in history. But I was living, first-hand, the theory of relativity. Thirty-one days on vacation, asking for another bottle of wine with dinner, passes much faster than thirty-one days in the University Hospital, asking people about their bowel habits.

I must have learned something during my first intern go-around, however, because my team, which included myself, and another ringer who had already completed her intern year in England, usually finished our work hours before the other teams with actual interns who were battling the hospital paperwork nightmare for their first time. Thus, I discovered that my intern year had not been wasted after all; I was now, surprisingly to myself, perceived as a strong medical team member on a notoriously tough service.

GERIATRICS & RUSSIANS

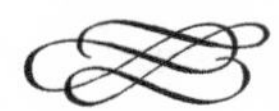

HOW TO COMMUNICATE TO MOTHER RUSSIA (FOR FREE!)

My next required rotation was on the geriatric service, which was going to be fun. I say "fun" not because of shuffleboard games or wheelchair races, but because there was no overnight call and no work on the weekend. I would not know what to do with so much free time.

Our days were spent examining elderly people and visiting their homes, checking for problems that would make it difficult for them to care for themselves properly—such as how they attempted to organize their buckets of medications. A study had determined that when the average person takes more than two medications a day, the likelihood of them taking the medication incorrectly increases exponentially for every added medication.

My clinic patients, who represented an average slice of American intelligence, usually admitted to screwing up taking a ten-day course of antibiotics. Even I, medically aware of the importance of taking medications properly, could never remember to take medicine as it was prescribed. Now imagine elderly people, perhaps already hampered with a degree of memory impairment, being prescribed eleven different medicines (some of which might further blur their cognitive function) which they need to take at different times of the day, with different frequencies, and try to guess how effective their medical regime really was. Now think about how ridiculous it is for their doctor to even venture making necessary modifications to those medicine regimes, not knowing how correctly, and therefore effectively, a patient was taking their medicine—or even if they *were* taking their medicines at all.

Inevitably these patients were labeled, "Noncompliant with medications," meaning the patient's problems were due to them not taking the medications as we had prescribed them.

The residents and attending physicians often chuckled about how difficult these "noncompliant" people made their jobs. The patients, meanwhile, didn't give a whit of sunshine about being labeled anything because they couldn't afford the medications anyway, and only took them every other day to save money—which made the medicine both ineffective and therefore a complete waste of money.

These geriatric patients, who usually struggled to tell me why they were even in the office, were up against a litany of prescription drugs, some for high blood pressure, some for pain, some for constipation, some for getting an erection—and they were supposed to know when to take them, and to remember which was for what.

My solution (ha!) would be to have a pharmacist invent a water-soluble fizzy solution with all a patient's medications mixed in, for the patient to down in one big gulp. Then again, I also think tequila should be studied for the medicinally beneficial Darwinian effects of killing off your body's weaker cells.

Anyway, we examined how geriatric patients dealt with their overload of drugs, and, just as problematic, but far more practical, how they prepared food.

I freely admit to being challenged by using a microwave, and here we had people who couldn't remember their children's names, using microwaves, and gas ranges to cook. I discovered that half the patients had eaten their meals raw or overcooked for years—and God knows what wine they were matching with that frozen potpie. Meanwhile, throughout that month, to break up the monotony of discussing pills and geriatric nutrition, I was, as always, forced to go care for my clinic patients.

Now let me speak of the Russians invading our clinic. Being connected with a major University hospital meant that many patients chose to use our clinic for their medical care. A host of underserved populations, populations that had never heard of medical care, let alone practiced anything healthy, were referred to our clinic from the hospital. Additionally, a large population of foreign-speaking people, who had possibly arrived from foreign countries, came to us for treatment.

The latter populations were very polite and seemed genuinely appreciative of the care they received from us. But the language barrier provided an interesting, not to mention time-consuming, obstacle.

A large population of Russians came to my clinic, and we were required by law to use a translator for visits with foreign language-speaking patients. This law seemed like a good idea, as I was not quite sure how we were to communicate otherwise.

When I had lived in France, I had been given two bottles of medicine when I was diagnosed with bronchitis (at least I think that's what the doctor said I had). To this day I have no idea how many pills I was supposed to take or for how long. I had just smiled and nodded my head as he rambled off instructions, then handed me two bottles of what I assumed was medicine—very much the same way my patients, English and foreign language speakers alike, smile and nod their heads at me.

With my Spanish-speaking patients, I used my modicum of Spanish to muddle through our time together—it seemed more personal than having a disinterested third-party translator on the speaker phone to interpret for us. I will, however, admit I constantly fretted that I had missed some idiomatic change in their reply, or a double negative, or sarcasm—any of which might drastically alter their medical care.

I became accustomed to asking simple questions like, "Tienes un tos?" while mimicking a coughing fit (My version of, *Do you have a cough?* Complete with physical reenactment). The patients often replied with a lengthy diatribe regarding the state of the economy in Mexico City, and something to do with hygienic reasons for not attending kid's films on Wednesdays.

I would nod my head through their lengthy, albeit troubling, responses, and then gamble on a reply: "Entonces, no tienes tos?" *(Then, you don't have a cough?).*

And if I had guessed correctly, they would say, "No" and feel good that I had listened so carefully. If however, they did actually have a cough, they appeared to shoot me a look of, *Have you not been listening to me, you toadstool of a piss-ant excuse for a doctor?* And then reply, very slowly, "Claro, tengo un tos." *(Duh, of course I have a cough).*

And so it went.

While I was able to make a real mess of the Spanish language and administer potentially horrendous care to these patients through mistranslation, I spoke no Russian, and therefore the Russians were safe from my "gamble on the grammar" approach that my Spanish-speaking patients risked.

When it came to Russians, the patient and I sat facing a speakerphone, and the Russian patient would start by rambling off the first three pages of *War and Peace*. It's apparently how you start traditional medical visits in Russia.

The speakerphone would then tell me, complete with staccato Russian accent, *"They want blood pressure medicines."*

Now, in most clinics, and with most patients, had they wanted blood pressure medication, I would have asked many questions regarding the patient's health, questions about their cardiac risk factors, how long they had been treated previously for high blood pressure, and would order the appropriate tests for patients with hypertension to check items like their cardiac status and kidney function.

I had attempted this proper medical approach with a Russian babushka one time only. The translator had carefully listened to all my important questions. She then threw out a six-word question, in what sounded like Russian, to the seventy-eight-year-old Russian lady in front of me, who in turn responded with a chapter from Tolstoy. (Come to think of it, maybe they were using the translation service as an inexpensive way of relaying news back to the motherland?)

The translator then barked at me, *"She says, 'No.' Now she needs blood pressure medicines."* At which point I chose to write a prescription for blood pressure medicine and be done with the entire charade—my next patient had already been waiting twenty extra minutes while we had contacted the translator.

This was Russian medicine at its finest. I would write a prescription for whatever they wanted: pain medicine, sleep medicine, blood pressure medicine, you name it. They asked, they received.

I did attempt to cover their basic medical needs, or at least go over their medical history, and occasionally convince them to get some baseline blood tests—which for some reason was considered a great inconvenience when they just needed some pills. *Silly Amerikan doctor.*

Once, however, my blood test insistency managed to catch a lady with CML (a type of leukemia)—and yes, *catch* makes it sound like she was trying to get away with something in the first place, which she likely wasn't—but that's how it sometimes felt with the Russian crowd.

The patient had come to the clinic demanding blood pressure medicine (I swear a Russian newspaper must have convinced all

Russians that blood pressure medicine was good for them—or perhaps they were getting it paid for by Medicaid and sending it back to Russia?). When I received this patient's blood work report, I recognized a mild form of blood cancer, and had to call and explain, via a translator, that she needed to come in and see me again to discuss her blood tests.

A week later we were sitting next to each other, staring at the speakerphone snapping at me, *"She wants more blood pressure medicine please."*

I finally asked, "What's with the blood pressure medicine? Honestly, she just got a month supply last week, is she giving it away?"

Total silence.

"Forget it, listen, I have to tell her about the results of her blood test."

"Do you want me to translate all that?"

"No... Just the part about the blood test."

The translator had a small conversation with the Russian patient, and then told me, *"OK, but then she will have blood pressure medicine."*

Good grief, Team Russia! "No. Listen, I need to tell her she has CML. It's a mild form of cancer, not a big deal, but—"

"Cancer?" the patient asked, clueing into the one big bad English word she recognized.

I turned to the patient as though she could, by this single word pronouncement, now understand English, "Cancer, yes, but it's not a *serious* cancer. You need to see a blood cancer specialist."

Which, to her ears, I'm sure, sounded like, "CANCER, blahblahblah CANCER, blahblahblah CANCER."

She started yelling at me in Russian with the word "cancer" thrown in for spice.

Meanwhile, I started shouting at the phone for the translator, "Tell her she just needs a blood specialist. A hematologist to follow up with her. Tell her it's *not* serious."

Apparently, the idea of needing to see this frightening-sounding specialist must have been akin to condemning her to scientific experiments in a gulag because she tried hyperventilating in order to pass out, before quickly going into another diatribe involving cancer while vigorously fanning herself with a magazine.

Finally, the translator yelled at us both, her words booming through the room (I was unaware that she could control the volume from her end of the phone) to shut up.

Somehow a deal was negotiated between the translator and the patient whereby the patient would go see the hematologist—but only *if...* I wrote her another prescription for blood pressure medicine *and* threw in a bonus prescription for sleep medicine.

I was aghast. I shook my head, snorted, wrung my hands, thought of the alternatives, and wrote the damn prescriptions—which the patient accepted as though she was granting me a favor.

In the end, the patient not only saw the specialist, but also eventually thanked me. She returned to the clinic and reassured me that everything was OK, that I really needed to understand that the cancer, called CML, was not so serious.

Specialists could probably afford to hire better translators, but oh man, I wanted to shout in any language I could think of, *"Yes, I know! That's precisely what I told to you!"*

FUN IN THE MICU

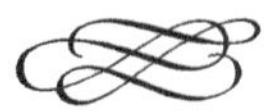

BALLOONS, TRIPS TO THE ZOO, AND GUMBALL MACHINES

I had, as you might recall, abandoned my brilliant plan of not proceeding with my second and third year of residency training. I now continued to make up all the terrible rotations I had avoided my first year with the belief that they would never be an issue. One such rotation was working in the Medicine Intensive Care Unit (MICU).

ICUs are inherently bad rotations for many reasons: 1) There's no crying in baseball and there's no sleep in the ICU. Call was scheduled every other night. 2) The people who ran the ICU were really smart, and they grilled young residents for breakfast. 3) Residents cried on these services. Imagine being on a television game show, and instead of merely being kicked off the air for losing, you were forced to stay for a month and be abused repeatedly for not knowing anything, repeatedly flogged for your ignorance. So with dread flooding my veins, I entered the ICU service.

The ICU was a routine and protocol-based unit, which made life somewhat easier. Once you knew the rules, everything worked pretty smoothly. Learning the rules and protocols, however, was not so easy. The day before I started, I called the chief resident in the ICU and was assigned patients to care for starting the next morning.

"You could come in and read over their charts tonight," he informed me.

Are you delusional? I thought, *I could also tromp naked across campus in a snowstorm.*

He continued, "But some of them might die overnight, so just get up here early tomorrow." So, like a good resident, and against all my desires, I arrived early in the morning (around 4:30 a.m.) to study my patient's charts and read up on the people who were to be under my watch.

The ICU itself was essentially a purgatory point for patients. From there, patients were either transferred onto a hospital floor if they improved, or received final transfer orders to move on, pass go, and not collect anything, if their health worsened.

First off, nobody in the ICU had any idea who I was that morning. I rarely worked in the University Hospital, and the ICU workers had not seen the light of day for decades; so we had never been properly introduced or broken bread together, and they did not seem altogether keen on meeting me now.

All I wanted was to read my patients' charts. Instead, I received scowls and looks of paranoia when I asked where to locate these elusive volumes of daily notes, orders, medication lists, and vital signs.

By the time I finally located the charts and skimmed their covers, I realized that the clock had rocketed forward, and I was supposed to be ready for morning report with the entire ICU team in half an hour, i.e. I was supposed to have actually seen and examined all my patients in the next thirty minutes. Not only was seeing the patients considered essential to their treatment, but I was also expected to know all about their medical care, to have a plan for their day, and to have written their morning notes, etc.

I had not the faintest clue what was going on with my patients beyond them being sick. I was, however, pretty confident that if my plan for their day consisted of a trip to the zoo followed by ice cream—I would not be making their plans for a second day.

Fortunately, the people that ran the ICU, despite their reputation for making people weep, realized that all newcomers were relatively ignorant of expectations. I was saved by several factors: first, I was fortunate to work with an amenable group of residents. They had already questioned their fellow residents about my reputation from preceding months (like any other aspect of life, residents were very concerned with who was on their team), and I had been viewed favorably as not only hard-working and efficient, but much more to my credit, as having a working knowledge of *Spinal Tap* and Monty Python quotations to apply to patient care. Secondly, as mentioned, the protocol-based treatments in the ICU made certain aspects of caring for patients more straightforward. Care was driven by following appropriate algorithms; thus proving, once again, that computers could probably do a better job than I.

LIKE EVERYWHERE ELSE IN THE HOSPITAL, THE MORNING STARTED with rounds, which consisted of pimping the residents on the nature of their patients' diseases, treatments, medications, ventilator settings, etc.—Socratic teaching applied with serious gusto. Every day we would decide on the patient's agenda for the day: maybe increase their calories in the feeding tube; or perhaps discuss a time to turn off both their sedation drip and ventilator to see if they could breathe on their own; or maybe just alternate a patient's antibiotics.

Literally ordering body function changes such as the depth and rate of breathing, ordering medicines and machines to control heart function, food rations, and such—all on a resident's scribbled piece of paper.

It was always a bit awkward to walk into a room and examine a patient who was unconscious, or at least sedated. You never knew if they would remember you or not as they lay prone, their chest rising and falling rhythmically with machines pumping and beeping, while you performed a physical exam, and a nurse changed their diaper.

Everything regarding their personal care was considered: keeping them comfortable; preventing their skin from breaking down; allowing no infection in the room; giving them adequate calories, yet not too many—it was a mathematical nightmare to calculate the massive and essential factors crucial to keeping them alive. And then, on a simple human level, it felt a bit odd talking to an unconscious person; but the nurses always let us know that the patients responded well to even those brief personal interactions.

I would walk into the room and say, "Hello Mary, it's Dr. Lawrence, just going to take a listen," and move aside the hospital gown to listen to her heart and breathing while she lay there, lungs pumping, filling with air from a machine. You had no idea if they could hear you; but the patients certainly seemed to calm down, and their heart rates decreased once they learned to recognize your voice. They would appear more at ease when people they knew were in the room, especially their family. It was a bit unnerving to see all these "unconscious" patients being kept alive with the help of machines—yet responding just enough to let us know there was still someone alive in their sedated bodies, and that they must be craving human interaction.

One late night a very sick patient arrived by ambulance. He had been quite ill when the ambulance picked him up from an outlying hospital and had worsened dramatically on the drive over.

He was now unconscious and intubated. He was what in ICU language would be described as "septic." We're talking super sick with high fevers, and a blood pressure that was bottoming out. If your blood pressure is low, you might feel lightheaded when you stand up too quickly. If your blood pressure is really low, you might not move adequate blood through your body, the pressure might not be enough to perfuse your organs, and you die.

The attending physician had not yet arrived, but the guy needed immediate help. I cannot quite remember why I was the only doctor present, most likely the team was working on another patient, but I figured I better get a femoral line in place right away. Typically, when people are very sick, the attending in charge liked to place these central lines (large-bore IVs with multiple ports) into a patient's femoral or jugular vein (large veins in your groin or neck respectively); but I was the only doctor present.

Placing a central line has a few risks as you are sticking a very large needle into a large vein running adjacent to a large artery that you do not want to sever. But I was mostly nervous because the patient was septic with a barely measurable blood pressure, making it more difficult to get a needle into his blood vessel (they shrink down without adequate volume or pressure), and there might not be many chances to do so as he was rapidly deteriorating. I felt that if I did not get this line in place quickly, we might not be able to successfully treat this dying patient.

I cleaned his skin and successfully inserted a large needle into his femoral vein on my first attempt. *Phew.* With the most troublesome step completed, I next inserted a guidewire into the needle and fed it into the vein. Residents had been known to let go of the guidewire, which then disappeared into the patient, causing havoc. I removed the needle (firmly holding the guidewire), made an incision in the patient's skin to allow space to thread the large catheter over the guidewire and deep into the femoral vein, then removed the guidewire. I sutured the catheter in place and stood up straight to relax my back, taking a deep breath of relief.

The ICU attending finally showed up and, having missed the fun of placing the first line, and assessing that the patient was critically ill, wanted to insert more central lines. He tried, multiple times and in multiple locations, but was unable to get a single other line placed because the patient's blood pressure had continued to drop so low as to almost collapse his blood vessels.

Overnight, into that one femoral line, the one I had fortuitously placed, was dumped 56 liters of fluids and blood products to counteract his sepsis, and keep his blood pressure up, thus saving his life.

I guess they save and lose enough lives in the ICU that nobody thought to congratulate me on having placed the one single line of access we had to use. And if you read that line again, the one about the patient receiving 56 liters of fluid, that's not a typographical error, he swelled like a puffer fish.

Another interesting case, a favorite of mine that month, involved an elderly lady, Mrs. Redding, who must have been in her eighties. She had white hair with an equally pale pallor and was toeing the line between life and death. She had developed idiopathic cardiomyopathy, an inflammatory swelling of the heart for unknown reasons. The end result of this disease was that her heart did not have the strength to pump blood around her body, i.e. she was dying of heart failure. Her several young family members sat by her bedside every day, knowing she was close to death.

I was most aware of her because a balloon pump had been placed in her heart to keep it pumping efficiently. A small balloon in her blood vessel would inflate at just the right time to keep her blood pumping smoothly enough to keep her alive. There were complex formulas involving physics and waveforms that we used to measure if the pump was helping. Formulas I understood for several seconds while they were explained to me. Formulas that actually make the NFL quarterback rating system seem comprehensible.

Each day, as our morning round party stopped by Mrs. Redding's room, I would stand a little farther back in the group, hoping not to be called on for yet another display of balloon pump ignorance by the attending.

And it seemed every day I would hear, "So, family practice resident, looking at this wave form, what would you change to improve her heart's efficiency?"

And in reply, I grasped for any of the correct answers I had overheard the previous day, such as, "Increase her cardiac output?"

"That's the goal, yes. Now, how would you do it?"

"With the balloon pump?"

"Didn't we go over this yesterday?"

"Yes."

"So?"

"I would, uh, re-float the balloon, and see if it could be more efficient?"

"Do you know what you're talking about?"

"Truthfully?"

"Yes."

"No."

"Somebody help Dr. Lawrence."

And the chief resident would explain, once again, how to correctly interpret the balloon pump waveforms on the screen in front of me.

"Does that make sense now?" asked the attending.

"Yes. But I can't guarantee I'll understand it tomorrow." I replied.

Complete honesty was essential to surviving the ICU—you didn't bullshit an ICU attending physician.

Another resident nudged me and whispered, "Don't worry, none of us understand it either."

One morning, however, despite our futile efforts to understand the balloon, things looked grim for Mrs. Redding. She appeared as close to death as I imagined anyone could look and still be breathing. Every medical sign indicated that there was no way for her to survive the morning. We told her children that their mother was going to pass away very soon, and that they needed to say goodbye. When I left to go home later that evening, she was still breathing, barely.

Usually when you arrived back the next morning, you discovered several new patients had been admitted overnight, and several had died. You showed up to discover Mr. Edwards in room 104 was now Mrs. Douglas. And so it went. But this next morning there was no Mrs. Douglas. Mrs. Redding was still there, and she shockingly had a tinge of pink to her usually alabaster pallor.

Hours later, during morning rounds, we arrived at her bedside, and she sat up to greet us. I was not even aware that she could move until this moment, let alone sit up; and then, to all our wonder, she told us she was planning on dancing in the halls that afternoon. She also looked thirty years younger (she turned out to be in her forties, which explained why her children looked like teenagers, despite all of us thinking she was close to eighty years old).

I have no idea what wonder drugs they had pumped into her overnight, but sure enough, she was transferred out to the hospital floor the next day with a rosy complexion.

But Mrs. Redding was the exception to our patients surviving. Many patients in the ICU were simply not going to stay alive. We knew it, but how do you gracefully pass on that information to family members? We would hold family conferences to openly discuss whether or not to continue their care, i.e., keep machines turned on, and medicines flowing, in order to keep the patient alive.

First, the medical team, without family members present, would meet and decide what we really thought was best, despite what the family would want. There was never a debate in these preliminary discussions—the medical team, knowing the patient was dying, was just collecting the objective information to tell the family that we did not think their relative was going to live much longer. Then we would call the family together for an open conference to discuss the patient's medical status.

Almost universally, when we had these family conferences it was because the person was indeed dying, and there was not much to be done, but in these last hours, the families would have huge dramatic fallouts. Cousin Louie would see no point in continuing unnecessary medical care; while Aunt Roberta, who had not talked with the patient in ten years, was suddenly the most attached of the entire family, and absolutely refused to let him die now. Maybe he still owed her money.

We would present the medical information, answer questions, listen to both sides argue over the care, and then leave to let them think everything over and talk amongst themselves. If we were holding such a conference with family members, it was almost always because multiple organ systems in the patient had failed and there was no real way back for them to recover.

Twenty-four hours later the families were almost always at peace with letting the person pass away comfortably. One astute family member would usually pull me aside and ask what I would do under their circumstances.

Looking at the patient on a breathing machine, stuck full of feeding tubes and fluid lines, I would think back to a Tennyson line, *"As though to breathe were life."* Not the way I would want to go...but then again, Mrs. Redding was dancing in the fourth-floor hallway.

I'M NOT SURE WHY THERE SEEMED TO BE A DIRECT CORRELATION between the intensity of the clinical rotation I was working in the hospital, and the irresponsible, childlike behavior I displayed outside of it—often coinciding with relationship difficulties.

Although, relationship difficulties were pretty much a constant, so I can't blame that on the intensity of work. There was a mythical number that only nine percent of relationships survived medical school and residency. None of mine did.

And sure enough, after months of delaying the inevitable, my relationship with the heroic, all-star surgeon was removed from life support. I had just moved into a house with Scott, he of the deflating lungs, who had also just broken up with his girlfriend the previous month. We welcomed a calming, new environment, and hoped to get our bearings in life somewhat straight again.

The same day my relationship ended, our new house flooded, for the second time. The first flood had been mild; this time the flood filled the basement (where I lived) with sixteen inches of water and required that the Hazmat crew spend the night. Several days after this aquatic debacle, we were scheduled to be at the Boulder Mountain Tour, a cross-country ski race in Idaho we traditionally attended with a large group of friends.

Scott left for Idaho in the middle of the week and proceeded to total his truck when he hit a deer on the drive north.

I followed two days later, slipped on ice outside the car and painfully sprained my wrist.

The night after the race, we—along with a large group of friends—got exceedingly drunk, and somehow, I ended up wearing lipstick and a wig out to a restaurant. On my way back from the restaurant's bathroom, with my wig looking great, I stopped at a table where my now ex-girlfriend happened to be sitting. I do not believe I was displaying the strong, confident life transition I had hoped to air in front of her, the staid and responsible surgeon looking with disgust at her drunken, lipstick-wearing ex-boyfriend, as he attempted to muddle out polite greetings to everyone else at the table.

To top off the night, Scott accidentally broke the restaurant's enormous gumball machine with his arm, slicing open his wrist in the process. This would have been a perfect time for me to show off my years of medical training and suture up my wounded friend. Fortunately, more rational friends decided my drunken enthusiasm was exactly the reason I would not be allowed to accompany him to the Emergency Room.

Wounded, hung-over, sutured, and depressingly single, we returned to our flooded damp home, Scott's destroyed truck and a misbehaving Labrador. Our bearings were far from straightened out. This was no way to go through life.

RADIOLOGY

THE UNDERGROUND LAIR OF UNEROTIC BREASTS

Requiring peace and solitude to settle what felt like a flailing personal life, I signed up for an elective rotation with the hospital's radiologists. Every morning I showed up in the dark caverns of their hermit-like radiology department, and every morning the radiologists stared at me with bewilderment, wondering who I was and questioning why in the world I would want to spend time in their recluse domain.

Truthfully, I was just enjoying a tame schedule without call. I did not believe, however, that the radiologists would appreciate my blunt reason for spending time with them. Instead, every morning I reminded them that I was a medical resident and had signed on for an elective with them to better learn how to read X-rays. You'd think they'd recognize me by now. I'd been visiting their murky grotto to review patients' radiology studies for two years. Maybe living underground had mussed their recall.

I genuinely did want to improve my ability to read these films because oftentimes, at 3 a.m. on call, a chest X-ray would be taken of a patient that had become short of breath. As the resident, you were supposedly able to properly interpret the X-ray to determine if the patient was having difficulty breathing due to pneumonia, heart failure, or perhaps fluid accumulating in their lungs for different reasons altogether, such as inhaling dinner down their trachea.

At 3 a.m. the radiologists were in bed and were not going to come see an X-ray for you—so you needed to learn what you were looking at on the X-rays to figure out the best treatment.

The following morning a radiologist would review all the films and send an official report—that way you could keep track of your guessing average. In most cases the last line of any radiology report read: *"The above findings might be due to an infectious process but cannot rule out fluid in the lungs from other process, including heart failure. Recommend clinical correlation."*

Which, not too loosely, translated as: *Figure it out based on what's going on with the patient, not the X-ray, and don't even think about waking me at 3 a.m. if they get worse. And P.S. Consider my ass covered no matter how you screw up.*

I figured that by spending a month with these guys, I would unlock their otherwise enigmatic reports, and learn to better understand X-rays—I was certain of it.

Instead, for those weeks, I was pawned off from one radiologist to another until inevitably, every morning, I was assigned to look over the shoulder of whichever radiologist was reading mammograms that day.

Breasts, breasts, and more breasts. Staring at negative images of breasts with a magnifying glass to see if there were any hints of malignant tissue present was not the slightest bit titillating—no matter how hard I tried.

The real radiology learning had happened back on the ICU rounds. During the ICU months we would enter the X-ray room every single morning and the intern (that was somehow always me) would stand and attempt to correctly interpret all the ICU patient's X-rays.

"Dr. Lawrence, you're the intern du jour, read the chest X-rays for us," intoned the Attending.

"Actually, I'm not an intern anymore."

"Just read the X-rays."

And I would start a proper X-ray presentation: "This is a chest X-ray for Mr. Jones, a sixty-four-year-old man with pneumonia who is currently intubated, ...blahblahblah...and the left lung field has a hazy opacity."

"Lung fields? Are you a cow? Fields are for cows. What are you trying to say?"

"That the left lung has an infiltrate."

"Then say it."

"The left lung has an infiltrate."

"No it doesn't, it's a hazy opacity."

Chalk up another humbling experience to good teaching. After two weeks of staring at breast tissue, and not learning to read the mysteries of a chest X-ray, I was on vacation.

I HEADED TO TELLURIDE, COLORADO, TO HOUSE AND DOG SIT FOR A friend, where I planned to write a movie script. I stocked the house with provisions: coffee, tea, tequila, dog treats, pasta, and was then unexpectedly snowed in under sixteen inches of new snow. Sounds idyllic and it was. I wrote and relaxed with two Labradors in the mountains.

The only real medical experience I had during my stay involved shock therapy, an experience I covered in an email to friends along with complaining of my inability to find anyone to go on a date with over a period of several months. Here is the pre-blog era email:

"The question at hand is whether or not I am a social moron and would perhaps benefit from something therapeutic, like shock therapy. I am not being flippant. I actually survived shock therapy today. Arriving

home from town, I was attempting to evacuate the dogs from the car, my arms filled with groceries, backpack, and some random junk. I was trying to get Max and Winston [the Labradors] out of the car when the neighbor's dog, Chelsea, showed up for the party. Winston and Chelsea started running laps in and out of the car, spraying mud all over me as I shouted at Max to get out of the car. But Max would not move because he was convinced he was still wearing his shock collar. The collar, however, had fallen in the mud. The groceries were falling out of my tired arms, and the other two dogs were going berserk, knocking me into the snow and mud as well. I picked up Max's collar to show him it was not on his neck.

ZAP!

I was shocked, literally, for my stupidity, and dropped the rest of the groceries in the mud. Perhaps this shocking-for-stupidity treatment could aid my pathetic pursuit of going on a date?"

So, there it is, negative breasts, electric shocks, and some rest for the month of April. Nothing too traumatic. The rest of the vacation was fortunately uneventful because next on the agenda was high risk OB, a rotation notable for the lack of any rest.

HIGH RISK OBSTETRICS

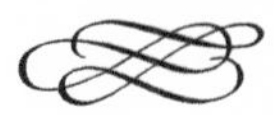

BLEEDING, ABRUPTIONS, AND BABIES —OH MY!

I was back on the University Labor and Delivery service for a month of "High-risk Obstetrics." Despite joining this exciting sounding high-risk team, the OB residents on the service took care of all the truly dangerous and exhilarating cases, while we family practice pissants took care of all their more routine OB patients. This division of care made sense because the OB residents would spend their career treating high-risk OB cases, while family practice doctors would refer any high-risk patients to those same doctors. That said, it was important for a family practice doctor to recognize what warranted a high-risk case in the first place so that they knew which patients were appropriate to refer.

So, what constitutes high-risk in obstetrics? Truthfully, I started believing that all pregnancies were high-risk. Our medical school embryology class had left me absolutely amazed that any pregnancies, any at all, lasted to term; and that they ever delivered healthy infants was truly wondrous. Turns out the majority of potential pregnancies do abort early, before anyone ever knows they're even pregnant—evolution's way of preventing pregnancies that would result in an unhealthy or unviable infant.

But high-risk OB dealt mostly with problems affecting the pregnancy in later terms. Issues on the mother's side included preeclampsia, hyperemesis gravidarum, placenta accreta, abruption, gestational diabetes, pre-term labor, maternal age, etc. Issues on the infant's side, as the wee babe innocently floated in utero (Major Tom can you hear me?), included: growing too big, too small, not having enough fluid around his or her spacesuit because they were not peeing enough, or having heart or kidney issues in utero...on and on.

And in case you are not sure, yes, the fluid that infants float around inside the uterus, their own personal hot tub, is filled with their urine. So don't feel too badly when your kids pee in a pool, it's innately part of survival.

It was truly amazing how many straightforward deliveries took place. Because, unless you were a perfectly healthy 21-year-old mother, you were considered high risk; screw it, you're all high risk, every pregnancy came with risks.

Now I'm exaggerating, but you get the idea. And regardless of what was going on, there was only so much that could be done. Mostly, the goal was to treat the current problem as best able and monitor the mother and baby really, *really* carefully. Then hope for a smooth delivery. Post-delivery, it was usually much easier to take care of the two people separately.

Let's return, for a moment, to those issues women may encounter when pregnant. What were all those crazy terms I just tossed about in a high-risk OB salad? Some were straightforward, such as hyperemesis gravidarum, fancy words for the mother vomiting excessively. With the hormone changes a woman experiences, there can be normal vomiting with pregnancy. We've all seen some television show where a woman vomits and suddenly everyone realizes she's pregnant. But, when she vomits non-stop, and medicines don't help, and she's becoming lightheaded and weak from extreme dehydration, then the baby does not receive enough nutrients and therefore cannot produce enough urine to properly float around inside the uterus.

While it's physically miserable to vomit several times, it can turn very dangerous for the mother and infant at the extreme level. Patients in this situation are set up with IV fluids and strong medicine to keep the nausea at bay. Essentially, it's another treat the symptoms, then watch-and- wait scenario. If it continues to be severe, the OB doctor gets them as close to term as possible, and then maybe induces labor to save some misery.

Similarly, if the pregnancy causes the mother's blood sugars or blood pressure levels to rise dangerously, the mother and child can both become quite ill. Again, it's watch and wait while the mother is given medicine to control those issues.

The uterus and placenta can cause a lot of dangerous issues together, as in the case of placental abruption described earlier in this book. The placenta is what attaches to the uterus and receives blood and nutrition from the mother that is fed to the infant via the umbilical cord. But what if the placenta grows too deeply into the uterus (both of which are packed with blood vessels), and in severe cases, keeps growing into nearby organs, like the bladder? This malignant placental growth, called placenta percreta, is very bad and very dangerous.

Or what if the placenta grows over the cervical os (the opening where the baby passes out through the uterus to be delivered)? Then he or she cannot get out, or might tear the placenta trying to get out, and cause profuse and dangerous bleeding.

Again, for a lot of those cases, you monitor the mothers carefully in the hospital until it is time to deliver, and then, well, the situation can become intense. Hopefully, and it's true for most cases, the baby is delivered, and that alone might settle the problem. Many times, for the more complicated cases, the OB opts to perform a C-section to avoid all the dangers that might occur with a normal delivery—and again, those usually go smoothly, and then it's easier to monitor and care for mother and infant independently.

So, despite the term "High-risk OB," it was mostly about managing high-risk situations to prevent them from ever becoming dangerous; and if you could handle these cases, normal deliveries become a walk in the park.

For weeks on the service, we had been carefully monitoring a woman with placenta percreta. Placenta percreta, as mentioned above, is a horrible condition where the placenta, acting like an aggressive cancer, grows through the uterus and into other body tissues. This situation is dangerous because the growing placenta is engorged with blood vessels, as are the organs and tissues it invades.

Placenta percreta is therefore very dangerous because if the placenta is cut, or if it bleeds, like it will when the baby is delivered, or with an abruption, then the mother would rapidly bleed to death—and if the baby was not delivered, it, too, would die from the sudden lack of blood.

This patient's particular case of placenta percreta was as serious as they come—not only was the high-risk OB team involved, but also the gynecology oncologist (who was running the show), along with the General Surgery team, and enough characters to perform *Les Miserables* if need be.

As explained to all of us on-call: if this patient started to bleed, then this case, if ever there was a case, warranted that we push her gurney down the hall at full sprint, and upstairs to the O.R., screaming the entire way.

This patient had, on several occasions, complained of mild abdominal pain that caused everybody to panic, as she was at high risk for a placental abruption. Then her pain would settle down and everybody breathed a deep sigh of relief.

Recall one of my very first cases on obstetrics as an intern, the case involving a term pregnant woman (39 weeks pregnant) with abdominal pain who had been turned away from her community clinic that morning because they were too busy to see her. Later that day, she arrived at the hospital to be evaluated for the same pain, and then started bleeding vaginally. We diagnosed her with having a placental abruption and performed an emergency caesarian section. But too late, the baby was already dead.

On that terrible occasion I became fearfully aware of abruptions, so much so, that I was always on the lookout for another possible abruption. A placental abruption occurs when the placenta pulls away from the uterus wall where it is attached, causing abdominal pain and typically vaginal bleeding. If a woman ever had vaginal bleeding, or abdominal pain, I would think to rule out an abruption-even if the person wasn't pregnant.

Remember however, that I am a family practice resident, biologically closer to a rodent than a doctor in these specialists' eyes (albeit a helpful and friendly rodent, perhaps), and I was never really put in charge of this specific patient's care with percreta; it was always handled by a senior OB resident.

In the middle of one of my call nights, a night when the OB residents had taken all the good cases and were off performing multiple C-sections in different operating rooms, I was left to twiddle my thumbs, and decided to go check in with the patient with the dangerous placenta, as we were supposed to check on her every hour.

As we were talking, she began to complain of abdominal pain, but she thought it was the same pain she had complained about on multiple previous occasions. I figured this was probably the same stuff that had caused everyone concern through the week, and that it would settle down, would just go away—I hoped, hoped, hoped, please, please, please just go away.

I checked her bed sheets and saw no blood—a good sign. Then, thankfully, her pain resolved.

A minute later I was called away to evaluate another woman we were watching carefully, one who had already experienced a small abruption.

I was wondering why I had to be on call tonight, and where were the other residents? The second woman turned out to be fine, she was just nervous, and wanted to make sure that a doctor would actually respond if she ever did have any problems and called for help.

I re-assured her that I was around if anything happened, to please not cry wolf again, and then I strolled back to the first patient, the patient with the precarious placenta percreta (how's that for high-risk alliteration?).

I figured if I kept checking on her, it would help her relax, and somehow that would help make sure there were no perilous changes in her status. Instead, when I said hello, she told me she was starting to experience the same abdominal pain again. Following protocol, I examined her.

And when I checked her bed sheets this time, I saw a trickle of blood between her legs.

If any blood appeared I had been told to run screaming.

I looked under the blanket again, wanting to make sure I was not experiencing a late-night hallucination, wanting to make sure I had seen blood, not a shadow, not a vision (*Is this a percreta I see before me?*)— before I made a complete ass of myself by running and screaming down the hospital hallways.

I lifted the sheet again—that was definitely blood. I had seen blood; I knew what blood looked like; yes, that was blood.

I then followed my orders and screamed. I screamed for a nurse. A senior resident ran into the room. He rechecked the patient's sheets, and promptly agreed with my expert assessment that there was indeed blood present.

We ran her gurney upstairs, racing and screaming like Paul Revere the entire way to the surgery O.R., calling for all the teams involved in her care, who came madly sprinting after us.

In the O.R., the specialist doctors were unable to get extra central lines in place. Central lines, the huge I.V. lines that run directly into the large blood vessels in the neck, would allow them to dump large volumes of blood and fluids into her body quickly when she needed it—which she was absolutely going to need when they cut away the encroaching vascular mess from her body.

Everyone knew she would bleed heavily, and they would need these large central lines to keep replacing her blood while they performed surgery as quickly as possible.

For some reason the doctors could not get the lines in place for an unusually long time. During this extended period, while we all held our breath, a small miracle happened. Her bleeding stopped.

Finally, a line was placed securely into her neck and literally, mere seconds later, as if on cue, her bleeding resumed. Except this time, it was not a light trickle, this time the floodgates opened, and a river of blood began pouring off the operating table.

It sounded like a kitchen sink overflowing onto the tiled floor.

Around the same time, I was called back to the labor and delivery deck. While I wanted to stay and witness (from afar) this ongoing surgery battle to save two lives, the truth was that I could not see anything happening because the OR was as crowded as a New York subway during rush hour. So, I wandered back downstairs through the now quiet hallways I had yelled through not long before.

The patient with the other possible abruption was now complaining that her pain was worse, and that she was bleeding vaginally. I hoped she was blatantly disobeying my request and just crying wolf again, because every single OB doctor and resident was either standing as close as possible to the bleeding woman downstairs or finishing a C-section.

I was the only doctor on an otherwise eerily quiet hospital floor, somewhat reminiscent of the famous hospital scene in *The Godfather,* when Michael protects the Don.

I quickly evaluated her for the mild bleeding (which was present), ordered some labs, and had her moved to a room next to the nurse's station for close monitoring. Her pain settled down and the bleeding stopped. *Phew.* My heart rate returned to normal, and I wandered back to the O.R. where I reported this latest development to the chief resident. He agreed I had taken care of the patient appropriately and we could continue monitoring her and her labs for now.

Hours later, the multiple surgery teams had excised the placenta percreta and safely delivered the baby. They saved both the mother and the baby's life that night, and in the middle of it transfused over 40 units of blood products. If you are not sure, that is a huge amount, maybe five times the amount of blood normally in her body.

Everyone survived on the OB ward that night. And while my miniscule part was limited to a bit of shouting for help, there was still something redemptive when I thought back on the woman with an abruption we had treated earlier in the year, when we were involved too late to save her infant. It didn't erase the memory, but seeing the good outcomes felt, while not joyous (I think most doctors would agree that they view even their craziest cases as just part of the job), at least satisfying. Which means it was time to move on.

PEDIATRIC ER

WHERE I PUT HUMPTY TOGETHER AGAIN

I returned to the children's hospital ER, where winter's respiratory infections had been traded for summertime accidents. Gone was the epidemic RSV season and the wheezing snot-nosed hypoxic little buggers it brought into my life. Not that you could ever see one too many infants with runny noses and wheezing lungs, but it was a welcome change to care for kids who had fallen into swimming pools (and fortunately survived), kids with springtime allergies, and the multitude of inept kids unable to stay upright on their bicycles, tricycles, rollerblades, and any other invention with wheels—God bless the latter, you are my people.

It was also springtime for adults, outdoor playtime. In one weekend stretch I had run a 17-mile trail race, the stupidity of which resulted in terrible blisters on the soles of both my feet. Hours after the race, I worked in the pediatric ER, where, due to the painful blisters on my heels, I walked around like a runway model on tiptoes for 12-hours. Between tired legs from the race, being dehydrated, and walking on my toes, my calf muscles seized up into spasmodic balls of agony.

I limped home from the ER at 2 a.m. and attempted to massage my sore legs because the next morning I was entered in the State bicycle Road Race. Trying to relax, I settled in to watch late night MTV in hopes of catching the sirens of Destiny's Child. They did not show up, leaving me asleep on the couch with a slobbering Labrador for company. Despite his brilliantly timed vocal alarm, his morning bark was a far cry from the searched-for, elusive "Bootylicious" video.

Remarkably, as I drove to the race, fortified with forty ounces of French roast coffee, a lot of Ibuprofen, and hopes of a good bowel movement, I felt quite good. Far less remarkable was how devastatingly short the effects of caffeine remained with me, and how quickly the reality of sore legs, exhaustion, a massive head-wind, and the desire to be back on the couch scanning the television for scantily clad singers, set in during the race.

I did not win, or come close for that matter, and even more painfully, I returned to the ER for another twelve-hour shift later that afternoon to painfully traipse around on my tiptoes. Despite the joy of caring for sick and injured tots, I anxiously looked forward to returning home that night to rest my sore legs and feet and to continue the search for any Destiny's Child video—that being the exciting extent of my romantic life. It was perhaps the distraction of the latter that allowed me to commit a rookie error.

My shift was almost over, and I sat comfortably watching the clock roll towards 2 a.m. I would soon be home. However, sitting without appearing to be busy is a mistake in any work environment, almost fatal in a hospital. The next thing I knew, a nurse was shouting for me to check on some kid in room 10 who had fallen off a fence.

Room 10 was where I found Christopher, a chubby, dirty, and bruised kid, who reminded me of a post-fall, Spanish-speaking, Humpty Dumpty wearing glasses and sporting a large laceration on his arm.

Why a ten-year-old had been running around after midnight did not concern me when all I wanted to do was go home. So instead of inquiring as to what mischief had produced the fall off the fence at an hour I hoped was past his bedtime, I simply explained that I was going to clean him up and put him back together again.

Christopher was not keen on my idea, and it took more than six repetitions of, "Yes, I am going to use a needle" for him to accept his fate of needing to weather my late-night tailoring skills.

In case Christopher and his incessantly loud denials that we didn't need to treat his almost six-inch long, very deep, and dirt-filled gouge was not enough to keep me entertained, I also had his mojito-infused mother, machismo father, and mischievous brother in the room.

There I was, exhausted, attempting with my pathetic Spanish skills to explain to the parents what I was going to do to close the 15-centimeter ragged cut in Humpty's arm, while his little brother kept trying to take my rolling stool away from me *as* I sat on it.

I explained to the mom and dad that seeing your own child's blood can sometimes make parents feel nauseated, so could they please relax and sit down (at least I think that's what my Spanish interpretation was close to saying). I assured them that we would be done in no time.

Typically, in this pediatric ER, the nurses (who are absolutely amazing at caring for and relaxing scared kids before a laceration repair) inject a mild sedative into the patient's nose. The effect of the medicine is to relax the patient, and often, as a side effect, it acts as a mild truth serum. I had witnessed a few rather hilariously embarrassing moments as teenagers spoke a little too openly to their parents. But tonight, the sedative appeared to have the opposite effect on Christopher.

During my description of repairing the wound, Christopher began to hyperventilate; the mother, who appeared to have taken the sedation owed to Christopher, waved her hand in some vague gesture that appeared to be calling for another cocktail.

Meanwhile, the dad stood up, beat his chest repeatedly, and swore, "Blood! It does not get to me!" And looking at the variety of tattoos he had received during prison time, I figured he probably could handle it just fine. I placed the father in charge of sitting on the bed to support, or distract, Christopher as I started the arm laceration repair process.

My first warning sign of impending disaster was when poor Christopher almost lost his mind when I gently washed the skin around the wound. The sight of the needle then increased his hyperventilation to a concerning degree. The subsequent screams from room 10 (our room), when I actually injected the lidocaine to numb his skin, brought several nurses running to make sure we were all OK.

The patient was fine. My nerves and ears were not. Then, after washing out the cut, picking out dirt, and profusely irrigating the laceration, I started to sew up the rather large wound in Christopher's arm, at which point his dad turned a shade of yellow not often seen during the summer tanning season. The *"blood does not get to me"* tough guy then started shaking, and proceeded to pass out, slumping to the edge of the table.

Christopher then completely flipped out. He did not know what was happening, and his dad was about to fall off the table. I was holding needles and suture in Christopher's skin, trying calmly to keep him from pulling his arm away from me, while his mom moaned sedately, wondering what had happened to her mimosa order.

And to think, had I merely gone to empty the trash bin rather than sitting doing nothing for two minutes, I would be home on the couch by now, fruitlessly scanning MTV for Beyoncé singing with her friends.

I turned to the younger brother, who had taken the opportunity of my standing, to steal my chair yet again, and asked politely, "Can you please go get the Nurse?"

He just stared at me, happily spinning on my chair.

So his mom translated my request into Spanish, "Llame a enfermera!" Even though the brother spoke English just fine.

And he just stared at her, so I told him in Spanish: *"Llama la enfamera!"*

And the mom translated my words back into English, *"Go call the nurse!"*

Meanwhile the dad had woken up and was now violently shaking as though he was having a seizure, which did nothing to calm Humpty down; he continued to freak out, shouting, crying, pulling away from me and my needles, and moving ever closer to falling off the table himself, which would just complete the famous wall-falling-off incident.

And by the way, the blisters on my feet *really* hurt.

Christopher yelling was not helping anyone, while Mom and I continued to take turns trying to out-shout each other in different languages to get the little brother to do something, as he now stood somewhat paralyzed at the closed door.

Finally, I triumphed by shouting, "*ABRE LA PUERTA*!" over his mom's "Open the door!" With the door open I finally shouted for some help in picking up the new casualty in the room, as the tough guy dad, having passed out yet again, had now slipped onto the floor.

This mess finally settled, I managed to calm Christopher with an in-depth discussion of Harry Potter, and put him together remarkably well for the size of his wound.

I made it home at 4:30 a.m., and once more was unable to find the sirens of Destiny's Child to woo me to sleep. And then I flew to Maui for a wedding.

What, pray tell, of medical interest exists in Maui that warrants a few paragraphs in this book? I could try and rationalize a medical study involving the effects of sleep deprivation mixed with high consumptions of caffeine and alcohol and their relationship to making an ass of yourself on a wedding dance floor—but I think Ireland and Greece went into cahoots on funding that study long ago.

I did, however, have a run-in with a wall of coral while surfing —a sport in which, like medicine, I find myself lacking in skills. Not surprisingly the coral won our encounter, leaving me with a deep puncture wound to my left shin.

I continued to fall off my surfboard for a few more minutes until the reality of attracting sharks with an open and bleeding wound entered my waterlogged skull, at which point the fun of floundering on the board took a downturn. I left my friends paddling around in the potentially shark infested, and now bloodied water, telling them I would return in a few minutes.

I drove to the closest town, Lahaina, seeking a medical supply store. A small pharmacy seemed to be the fix and I inquired about buying some suture material to sew myself up. They politely refused, and I settled for some gauze and hydrogen peroxide.

Settling on the sidewalk, I started to wash out the wound, when much to my surprise, I saw my bone staring back at me. I decided that sutures and maybe even some antibiotics would be a good idea, and reluctantly checked myself into the local Family Practice clinic—reluctantly because I had no idea how I would pay for this new expense; the trip itself had topped out my credit card.

A more thorough irrigation and several sutures in the leg later, I was placed on antibiotics and told by the bonny little family practice doctor not to go into the water for ten days.

"Well that's a stupid idea," I told this obviously delusional physician, "I just arrived here for a wedding and plan to windsurf and surf all week."

"Let me put it to you this way," she responded, "It would be really stupid for you to get in the ocean water here and end up with a bone infection."

I was never too bothered by my own stupidity, and told her as much by asking, "So, on the offside that I will be getting into the water, any recommendations?"

No, none.

I met her partway and took the rest of that day off from the water. I returned to the world of aquatic floundering the next morning with duct tape wrapped around my shin. My evenings would then be spent washing grit from the wound.

And suddenly, under-slept, dehydrated, and limping on a sore leg, it was time for me to return to residency training. But I was just getting my windsurfing skills above the level of frustrated-break-your-gear beginner who stood in the water and cursed the sport, to frustrated-hurt-your-gear-and-yourself intermediate who sailed far enough away to drift in the ocean and curse the sport.

This sudden improvement had been augmented by the fact that the Kanaha beach area was heavily populated for a three-day women's windsurfing camp.

While everyone else enjoyed our last night's dinner, I was burning cell phone minutes being transferred from one Delta airline ticketing person to another in an effort to change my ticket for one more day in the paradise of windsurfing mecca and women's windsurfing camp—not that I ever actually spoke to a single member of the camp.

All seemed futile as the last bar on the phone battery blinked warning signs, and the ticketing agents repeated that my ticket was not alterable for any reason whatsoever.

One last transfer, and an indignant woman asked me, "Why should we change your ticket, it's not refundable, alterable, changeable, nothing. What makes you think we can just do this for you?"

I broke down and pleaded my honest case, "Look, I don't have a lot of fun in my life right now. I don't get many days off, and I am having a really good time for the first time in a long time, and I just want one more day here. That's all I'm asking, please."

And she changed my ticket.

A few more quick calls and I had another resident working for me in the ER and had one more day to practice my newly blossoming windsurfing skills.

Within that twenty-four-hour extension, I broke my rented board and harness, bruised my ribs, added a few massive contusions to my thigh, terrified several women's windsurfing camp members by almost running them over with my board, and gained several liters of injected seawater into my brain, before returning to several more weeks of tending the town's injured tots in the ER.

Thank you, kind Delta lady.

The power of several days off to play in the sun and water proved quite rejuvenating. I returned home, went back to the ER, and for the first time, was, dare I type it out loud, consciously aware that I almost knew what I was doing. When I presented patient cases to the attending doctors, discussing my assessment and plan, they just looked at me wondering why I was wasting their time. It was a look that said, *"You know what you're doing, go do it. Just ask if you're not sure of something."*

So I did.

Which made sense. I was weeks away from being a senior resident, which meant I was expected to lead and teach the resident teams. And now, looking back, I realized, over the last months, I had already stepped into that role, teaching the medical students on our teams, because I knew what I was doing. Holy crap, I actually knew what I was doing.

My crowning achievement, besides suturing a lot of kids back together again, was an infant spinal tap.

Besides being one of the all-time greatest mockumentaries, *Spinal Tap,* whose timeless quotations helped me survive on the pulmonary team, also refers, predating the film, to inserting a needle into a patient's back, between the bones of their spine, and into the spinal canal, which contains the spinal cord (nerves descending from the brain) as well as the fluid that fills that canal and surrounds the brain, cerebrospinal fluid (CSF). It does not take much imagination to think of the potential dangers of such a procedure.

When a newborn infant, around two months or younger, is brought to the doctor because they have a fever, it is 1) difficult to assess the patient with questions as they only seem to reply by yelling at you, vomiting on you, or, far more concerning, lethargically not responding much at all; and 2) it's important to figure out what is triggering the fever in these patients. A fever in newborns is rare as they don't typically get out much, and are protected from a host of infections by their mother's immune system (for a few months they inherit maternal antibodies that make sure they don't pick up every new infection they are exposed to); their little bodies cannot handle too much stress just yet, and a fever at that age can come from infections like meningitis, an infection around the brain or central nervous system.

If an infant has a constant fever over several days, it's critical to diagnose what is causing it, and there are standard tests to order: blood tests, urine tests, a chest X-ray to rule out pneumonia; and the big daddy of them all, the spinal tap—words that terrify parents to hear. And while spinal taps used to be standard protocol for newborns with undiagnosed fever, there are currently questions regarding the need to do them for all such cases—but at this time, they were part of the fever package.

A spinal tap, inserting that needle into the canal hosting the CSF and spinal cord, allows a doctor to assess the pressure inside the canal (too high could signify some dangerous process causing swelling in the brain); and to drain off some CSF to test in lab for the presence of white or red blood cells—respective signs of infection, i.e. meningitis that requires immediate treatment as it can be life-threatening, or a potential hemorrhage in their brain.

Late one night, with an infant who had been feverish for days and was now slightly dehydrated, we decided it was necessary to perform the dreaded spinal tap. Cutting to the chase, I explained what we were doing and why to the parents, along with the risks involved. A nurse then helped hold the infant on his side in a slightly curled-up position to help open space between his lumbar vertebrae. I prepped the skin, marked the landmarks I would use to determine where to insert the needle, and pushed the long needle in between the tiny lumbar bones. Then I felt the slight "pop" as the needle entered the spinal canal. Some cerebrospinal fluid was drained off and sent to the lab for analysis.

The results returned a little later, and fortunately showed no signs of meningitis, and no red blood cells.

The zero red blood cells part of the lab report was notable on two counts. First, for the patient, no sign of red blood cells was a good result. Secondly, when you perform a spinal tap, sticking that large needle through the skin and into the spinal canal, there are multiple places where the needle might cause some bleeding, so it's typical and normal to see several red blood cells in a spinal tap.

If, however, you perform the entire procedure perfectly, and zero red blood cells show up in the tap, it is called a "Champagne Tap," and supposedly if you performed a champagne tap, you were gifted a bottle of champagne.

And there it was, for the entire ER staff to see, I had performed a champagne tap. We were in Utah, so I never received a bottle of champagne, nor was I hoisted onto the team's shoulders and paraded through the cafeteria, and nobody sang, "Hip-Hip Hoorah!"

However, the ER attending that night, a super cool guy respected throughout the medical community, a guy who made me think I might want to work in the pediatric ER, saw the result, glanced up at me, very subtly nodded his approval, and said, "Champagne tap. Well done."

Tell you what, for several minutes thereafter, I actually felt like a real doctor.

One further side note to bring me back to reality, the Lahaina Doctor (back in Hawaii) turned out to be absolutely correct. After ignoring her advice and playing in the water, my punctured leg developed a very nasty infection, and I was placed back on a second two-week course of stronger antibiotics.

Nobody ever said doctors knew how to take care of themselves.

EPILOGUE

So, there it was, I had completed my first years of residency, was about to become a senior resident, and after all this time, finally started to think I knew what I was doing. Once again, there was no fanfare between the years, you merely completed one rotation, and the next day started work on the next rotation, but now, as the senior resident, with heightened expectations of both working independently and leading the resident teams.

Despite the lack of any defining moment to mark the transition—which, after starting medical school with the head injuries, then making a potentially deadly error right before starting residency—I was quite content with this gentler shift instead of the traumatic and poignant moments. However, a significant change had occurred in all of us, a change we didn't really see or feel. All of us were now operating (poor pun) and thinking not just more efficiently, but also with more self-assurance. We started to believe that we knew what we were doing (caveat: that is in regard to professional life; I never knew what I was doing in my personal life).

And there was an interesting observation passed to us from the attending physicians. The intern year was rightfully the steepest and most massive educational curve encountered in medical training. You started out barely knowing what you were doing, and twelve months later after a non-stop barrage of work, teaching, and ingestion of volumes of information, you were thinking and working like a doctor. Then, over the second year, without knowing it, you were acting with more confidence, taking all that learning and experience, and applying it to cases which you had seen, and could now approach with aplomb, knowing your hospital team was present as backup.

But then you became a senior resident, and perhaps due to the psychological effects of knowing you were soon to be acting independently, in charge of patients and the residency teams, confidence actually dropped as residents started questioning all their own decisions, wanting to learn as much as possible before graduating. You therefore actually experienced another big learning curve in your last year.

I don't recall any conscious shift in my thinking, apart from believing it would be fun to be chief resident. But then the role of chief was dropped on my shoulders, and like a Greek tragedy, my chiefly pride went right before the falls. And that is where *PLAYING DOCTOR; Part Three: Chief Resident* takes us, with me acting confidently and falling on my face for all to see.

(Coming Soon: Playing Doctor Part Three: Chief Resident)

NOTES

ACKNOWLEDGMENTS

Thank you to my amazing wife for her love, patience, and support. I am so fortunate to have the love and support of our three wonderful kids. Thank you to parents who supported me and my education, and to my friends who always believed in my crazy ideas to write, to act, to become a doctor.

To Hoke, continually raising the bar on living. To Chris, for keeping me accountable and continually inspired. Brad, reminding me there is one acceptable way to practice medicine, the right way.

Thank you to all the patients over the many years who trusted me with your wellbeing and health.

Thank you to all the teachers, doctors, staff, that have instructed me over the years and had the patience to put up with me.

These books are so much better thanks to my editor, Anne Cole Norman.

The cover designs, which always make me laugh, are due to the wonderful creative talents of Caroline Johnson.

The marketing and planning are thanks to the lovely and brilliant Louise Newland.

ABOUT THE AUTHOR

John loves his family, his friends, skiing, biking, running, cooking, writing, traveling, and watching films. John received his M.D. at the University of Utah, which is where he also completed his residency training. He received a B.A. from Georgetown University—where he did not take a single pre-med class.

John has been a river rafting guide, ski race coach, assistant soccer coach, bagel baker, environmental entrepreneur, screenwriter, film director, and expedition doctor.

He attempts to stay healthy, but still falls off his bike (a lot). Fortunately, his wife and kids are there to pick him up.

CPSIA information can be obtained
at www.ICGtesting.com
Printed in the USA
LVHW031210160622
721427LV00003B/268